LION'S DEN
1950

MUM

The LION'S DEN

Bert Cummings

Published by R. H. & B. M. Norman,
12 Gloucester Street, Whitfield, Cairns, N.Q.

Printed in Australia by Watson Ferguson and Co., Brisbane.

First published by Angus and Robertson, North Ryde, N.S.W., 1985

Reprinted by the author, 1989

Reprinted 1992

Cover and Illustrations by W. Cummings

ISBN 09 593783-9-1

Warning: HEALTH HAZARD

The public is hereby warned that no responsibility will be accepted by the writer for any damage to health in the way of strokes or broken ribs caused by the reading of this story.
It is an express condition of the sale/purchase of this book that the reader does so at his own risk.
Quid rides? Mutato nomine de te fabula narratur.
Anyway, why laugh? This story could be about you.

THE LION'S DEN

1

One day, long ago in the dreamtime of the late sixties, I'm standing quietly in the bar, when I see a couple of urgers pull up in a battered old VW Kombi van, and not only does she appear to be chock-a-block with gear inside, which I can see through a porthole in the side of the van, but she has a heavy deckload as well. It appears they are carrying just about everything but the kitchen sink, and for all I know they may have that in amongst the gear too.

After a bit of a talk goes on between them — probably fanning themselves to see if they've got the price of a couple of stubbies, or maybe discussing the possibility that I may not have the bloody hide to charge for beer at all in an old joint like this, which from the outside looks more like a broken-down cane cutters' barracks than anything else — they finally unwind themselves out of the old bomb and slouch into the bar.

I say, "G'day," and they answer in the same strain, but don't appear as if they are going to be over-friendly. They have the usual haircut which proves straight away that they are crooked on all barbers, though what they've got to be crooked on those poor bastards for I don't know. After all, sometimes they give you a good tip for the TAB, even if they do give you a lousy haircut. The rest of these blokes' rig goes well with the long locks; like the grubby T-shirts, and the blue snake-proof strides that are only just managing to hang onto their bums, as though they have just crawled through a rather neat hole in a K-wire fence and haven't stopped to hitch their strides up afterwards.

One bloke says, "A couple of middies please," as though they haven't stopped anywhere in this State since leaving New South Wales. Mainly an act of course, expecting me to say, "Oh, you boys come from Sydney do you?" but instead I say, "Sorry mister, we only have stubbies."

"OK," he says. "Two stubbies."

I say, "What sort?"

He says, "What sort of beer you got?"

I reply, "Well, there's VB and NQ and Fourex and Pipeline."

He says, "What's Pipeline?" to which I reply, "It's really Cairns draught beer but instead of laying a pipeline all the way up here, they send it up in stubbies."

So they order a couple of stubbies of Pipeline, plonk their arses on barstools, and their filthy feet too, and commence to suck the beer. I realise now that they are crooked on shoe manufacturers as well, and possibly the bloke that makes hats into the bargain as I don't see any head gear around, although they could have hats in the Kombi. In the meantime they are eyeing off everything in the bar and getting ready to ask the same damn-fool questions that they all do.

In fact I could bloody near have a tape ready for them like they do in the cities with those phone answering services which start off say, "This is a recording".

You've got to be pretty easy natured to run a busy pub up here; not like the city where the publican doesn't muck about with anyone that plays up, just calls the coppers.

Here it's different; first of all if you're going to strong-arm the lot of them, you want nothing less than a light-heavyweight title to back it up, and that rules me out. The only title I've got is my birth certificate, as a sort of excuse for being on earth.

Well, these jokers ask a lot of questions as usual about the old bottles and things on the shelf, and I pull down one bottle which was made for the old New York Hop Bitter Company. I say, "This one goes back a bit," and point to the Yank flag on the bottle. "There are only twenty stars in the flag."

One bloke says, "What's that mean?"

I say, "Don't know really, maybe they were a bit short of stars those days." He gives me a sidelong look to see if I'm having him on, but I keep a straight face and it's got him wheeled.

I see him fingering the permanent two-bob piece on the counter — which is an automatic reflex with this type where any loose change is concerned — only this two-bob piece isn't really loose change, as it's bolted down. Originally I had one there glued on, but they soon shifted that. This one I got silver soldered onto a bolt with a dirty big nut and washer under the counter. It will take some shifting.

Suddenly one bloke says, "Christ. What is that animal there?" I swing round quick, thinking I'm being sneaked up on by a brontosaurus or something, but he's only pointing to a stuffed little native cat hanging on the wall.

I say, "That's only a wild cat." Before they can think up another question, I throw into the ring that the cat is peculiar in that he is one species that has no anus.

I let this sink in for a while and sure enough one bloke bobs up with the stupid question, "But how does he do his job?"

"He can't. That's what makes him so bloody wild."

One bloke says, "Smart, eh?"

I say, "Not really. Didn't you ever hear that one before? I fell out of the cradle and broke a couple of ribs laughing about that."

I can see I would be no good as a public relations man, because these blokes are getting a bit on the prod, so as a diversion I say, "Well, if you boys don't want another beer, I'll just go out the back for a minute."

One bloke says, "Who said we don't want another beer? Two more stubbies, sport." After he hears me get 'em out of the fridge, he sings out, "Make it VB this time."

So I put the stubbies back in the fridge, open the other fridge and get out a couple of VBs. When I knock the heads off them, I say, "Makes you feel more like being at home eh?", but they don't bite on this one. They're being a bit cagey about letting on where they come from, so I decide to tell them a couple of yarns anyway.

"One time I went down to Sydney, and I'm trying to get on an electric train to go out to a place where I had to visit a bloke I know. I get swept up in the rat race at Wynyard Station, and when I get to the ticket puncher, I ask him which train to catch. He says, 'You don't have to catch trains here mate. They're already caught. All you have to do is get on 'em."

"I get a bit snakey inside with this exchange, but I keep my cool, I say, 'OK. Which one do I get on?'

"He hooks a thumb over his shoulder. 'Turn left and you'll be right,' he says. 'If you turn right, you'll be left.'

"I move off saying, 'You're bloody smart aren't you?'

" 'No,' he says. 'Smart's on holiday. Brown's the name.' You've got to be bloody quick with these Sydney types.

"Another time I get as far as Melbourne and I go down to Flemington to see the Caulfield Cup run as I had a good tip . . ."

One bloke breaks in and says, "Listen old fellow, for your edification, the Caulfield Cup is run at Caulfield — not Flemington."

"Not the time I'm talking about. That was in 1944 and the Army was in occupation at Caulfield. They had to run the Cup — war or no war — so they ran it at Flemington." I see them exchanging a sly glance, but as this is probably before they were born, they can't argue about it. You can almost hear the wheels turning in their skulls. I'm two up on 'em now and I can see that they are going to get ready to retaliate before long, but I carry on with my yarn.

"Just when I'm trying to get in the gate, I get bumped to one side and a couple of big demons elbow their way through, flashing badges under the lapels of their coats and spitting 'Pleece' out of the corner of their mouths. The gatekeeper gives them a sort of mean look through crunched teeth, but doesn't say anything.

"Just then a little wizened-up joker sidles through straight after them, flips his lapel and says, 'Pleece pimp.'

"The gatekeeper makes a grab for him, but misses. He's too slippery. I don't think the gatekeeper tried very hard because by the look he gave the demons I think his great-great grandfather must have come out on the First Fleet, thus giving him a built-in allergy to coppers. You have to be careful with these Melbourne coppers. They have no sense of humour at all."

By now I'm convinced these two jokers have come from Fitzroy or Carlton, so I chuck another bit into the ring; "In fact, they can be real mean if it comes down to tin tacks. Still I suppose you can't blame them being proper bastards — when you think of the type of bloody mongrels they have to deal with."

I can almost hear the hair getting up on the back of these blokes' necks, but they play it cool. One bloke says, "How did you know they were demons?"

"How do you know anything when you see it? Like a

horse, or a cow, or a hippie. You just know." I go on, "You can get tricked up of course sometimes — like in Brisbane one time I saw a bunch of tram drivers. I thought they were a detachment of the Foreign Legion; and the coppers there on point duty looked like railway engine drivers. They have proper uniforms there on the engines — not like those lousy bludgers in New South Wales who get around in greasy overalls.

"The coppers now have got a new outfit, and they look like Blue and White Taxi drivers away from their cabs. This is only to trick the mob of course. It's so you won't take much notice of them when you walk against the traffic lights."

One bloke says, "How did you get on at the Cup anyway?"

"All right. I won a few quid. Mainly on the favourite at about sixes, but I backed another donkey at a hundred to one — I think his name was Paul or something. Anyway, he jumped out and led the field all the way, until about the two-furlong pole, where they usually sort out the donkeys and hairy goats from the real horses, and up bobs the favourite to win by a length. For a while I thought this other thing was going to get up and win, and I had ten quid on him at the price. I was just thinking of the 'grand' I was going to collect when the favourite romped in and I had to settle for about 150 pounds. Wasn't a bad day just the same."

By now the stubbies these jokers have drunk are starting to take effect in more ways than one. One fellow asks, "Have you got a toilet here sport?"

I wearily point down to the end of the verandah. "Yeah. Down the end there. Turn right and you'll be right." I feel like telling him, "No. We just do it under the mango trees," and wonder if they have a spare throne amongst all the junk in the Kombi for just such an emergency. "Have you got a toilet?" The bloody hide of him. Still, perhaps where he comes from they might be short on facilities like this.

While he's away I draw the other bloke's attention to the tail light on the van, which has come adrift from its moorings and is ready to fall off. "You want to get that fixed as soon as you get to town."

"What? The coppers bad in there?"

"Real savage. Why only last week they pinched a bloke

for having a tail light without a bicycle." I leave him to chew this one over while I go in to pack a few more stubbies in the fridges.

Just then I hear a bit of a rumble outside and look out to see a battered old Land Rover pull up. Out springs a bearded monster from the hills who I recognise as the Irishman, a tin scratcher from up round Mt Misery.

He comes breezily into the bar saying, "Hallo, hallo, hallo, hallo."

"How are you?" I ask.

"VB. Not too bad."

The other bloke in the bar gives him a sidelong look and turns back to studying the label on his VB, as though he has never seen one before.

As I knock the top off the beer, the Irishman says, "What's wrong with that bloke?"

"Nothing. He's just acting natural."

"Have a drink, mate," says the Irishman.

"There's two of them," I chip in, not wishing to miss a sale.

"There couldn't be," says the Irishman. Just then the other type comes back into the bar and slides onto his perch. Irish says, "The two of yer, have a drink with me. Fill 'em up, boss."

I don't know whether they mumble assent or not, but I have two stubbies on the bar with the tops off before they can wink.

"Cheers, mates," says Irish, downing his stubby with a long, steady gurgle, then plonking it down on the counter. "Again," he says. "A man gets dry up in those hills, even though most of the time he's up to his guts in water."

When I put the other stubby down, I say, "What about some dough?"

"What's that?"

"Loot, brass, bullion, whatever you like to call it."

"OK, I'll give you a cheque in a minute." Knowing him to be quite a good payer, I let it ride for a while.

One of the other blokes grins weakly at my crack at the Irishman. Pointing to another sign over the shelf he says, "What's that sign read up there?"

"Noli illegitimi carborundum."

"What's that mean? Latin isn't it?"

"Yeah. Sort of low Latin actually. It means 'Don't let the bastards grind you down.' " They both manage a bit of a sickly grin at that — like a cat that's stuck his jowls into a pot of lime-wash instead of milk.

Irish chips in now, saying. "Where do you blokes come from?"

They don't answer right away, so I cover up the awkward silence by saying, "Paddington, wasn't it?"

One bloke wheels on me; "What's wrong with you? That's in Sydney."

"That's right," I say. "I always get those two villages down there mixed up."

"Well," says Irish, "let's have another drink. Whose shout is it? Doesn't matter. I'll shout. Fill 'em up."

So the two blokes who were trying to out-fumble each other relax and wait for me to set up another round. This time they have the decency to toast the Irishman.

Just then a vehicle goes by at about thirty, and I miss getting a glimpse of it. "Who was that?" I ask.

"That bloke from up Mt Hartley with the pump and engine plant," says Irish.

"He's got a bit of a nerve; bypassing the place like that. I've got a mind to book him down for a drink."

"Put him down for two," says Irish. "He owes me one."

Just now the two urgers decide they're going to bail out, and start swallowing the last of their stubbies. The Irishman gulps his down too, just as though it was going out of fashion. As the blokes ease their behinds off their stools, he says, "Where did you fellows say you came from?"

"We never said."

"More like Never Never," said Irish. "Never shout and never refuse. Well, goodbye, sports. Have a good time back in Footscray, or is it Carlton?"

In the meantime these blokes shoot through and climb into the Kombi ready for a quick getaway.

"Ah well," I say, "perhaps they haven't got enough to return the shout. Either that or they've got to keep what they have to buy petrol in case they can't syphon off some bloke's tank on the way."

"I think we won that round anyway," says Irish, "even if it did cost me a couple of beers."

Next thing the Kombi takes off with a stuttering roar, like a Saturn rocket with only half its systems "go".

"Maybe," I say. "I better look in the bathroom first, to see if they knocked off the soap."

"Don't be silly," he says. "You don't think they'd use soap do you?" Then he thinks it over and says, "You might be right. I'll go and have a look."

He comes back in a minute and says, "You're right. They did!"

"Well," I say, "all in a good cause. Maybe one of these days they might get a grounding in basic hygiene — especially if they can keep getting free soap."

Just then another vehicle pulls up. It's so battered it could have been in one of those multiple freeway pile-ups, where every bloke in it is in the space race — you know, with about six inches of space between bumper bars.

Out piles a couple of long hairs, and I say to the Irishman, "Christ, here's a couple more of 'em. Just look."

He has a quick look out of the bar and says, "No. There's only one of them — the other one's a bird."

They range up in front of the bar, and the bloke strides manfully in, but the bird hangs back a bit at the door, just as though she had never been in a bar before. You can see with half an eye she's the sort that hangs round those Kings Cross bistro joints, which is only French slang for a sly grog joint anyhow.

"You can come in," I sing out, just to make it easier for her. "We don't mind ladies in the bar." So she sort of slinks in, and after one look at the wild Irishman, edges up near the hippie type, perhaps for protection. Not that he is much better to look at than the Irishman, as he has been dodging the barber for about three years. He must have missed his National Service callup, otherwise they would have had his mane off quick smart.

Into the bargain he's got a growth of beard that would put some of those old biblical characters to shame, and a pinched-looking nose on him covered with white sunburn cream which he's had to put on after laying about too long in the sun in contemplation. He's got a fair sort of a body on him — in fact he's built like the proverbial brick outhouse — but his general appearance is of a white-nosed rat chewing its way out of a bale of cotton waste. Like all these characters, he's a complete stranger to soap and water.

I have a quick look at the bird while I'm waiting for them to make up their minds what they want. She looks as though she could do with a good scrub down as well, and it's not all road dust either.

Her friend finally says, "Two beers please."

"Sorry, only stubbies."

"Well, two stubbies."

So I go to get the stubbies, and the bird pipes up and says, "Oh, I couldn't drink a full stubby," but I think to myself . . . I'd hate to see her get her claws on a full bottle of Gilbey's gin!

I say, "What's it to be?"

He says, "I'll have a stubby; NQ will do. What will you have, dear?"

She turns to me and says, "Could I have a gin squash?" Picked it in one.

"Sure," I says, and dish up the drinks. How they can drink gin at all I can never figure out, especially to get really on it. It's the only drink I know which makes all my little troubles big ones the next day. Still, everyone to his own poison.

The Irishman has been sizing the pair up, and he's one of those sociable sort of blokes who can be friendly with anyone, so he says as an opening gambit, "What's the road like coming up, mate?"

"What road? I didn't know there was one."

"You're right, mate," says Irish, "I meant the cleared space between the trees that you come along."

"Probably be a good road," says the hippie, "when they build it." This thaws the atmosphere a bit, and the bloke says, "How is it from here on to Cooktown?"

"Orright; there's only two bad spots. From here to the Black Mountain, and from the Black Mountain to Cooktown."

The hippie gives a bit of a belly laugh at this, like a horse jogging along with too big a gutful of water; and the bird simpers a bit, still sucking her mother's ruin through a straw while her eyes flick around at the old bottles, etc.

Anytime now I can see me getting pulled into the deal with the usual idiot questions. It's a relief sometimes to get a dozen in the bar at once so a man can escape this sort of thing, being too busy for them to buttonhole you. When they come in relays they can get at you, like the mob at Taronga Park around the monkeys' cage. No wonder the monkeys have developed certain mannerisms which are considered extremely rude.

Just then the bloke says, "Have you got a glass?" I go and get him a glass as I can see he's having trouble getting his stubby down. How he thinks it's going to be any easier to swamp it by being measured out in small quantities, I don't know.

I'm crooked on these jokers that want a glass, first of all because they make unnecessary washing up, and then because they just spoil good beer when they don't take it in its wild state, straight out of the bottle. Apart from that it's far more hygienic as you know no other type has had his dirty mug on your stubby.

I slip out of the bar for a minute and let the Irishman give them a bit of a lug bashing at which he's pretty good. When I come back in he's pressing them to have another beer — on him — but the hippie is not having any fights clear, and the bird is backing out of the bar. The bloke is shaking the Irishman's hand and saying, "We must really get going."

"Get going?" says Irish. "Christ, I thought they were Way Out already."

Well it takes all sorts to make a world. They take off in their battered jalopy, and Irish says, "You better get yourself one."

I take a quick look through the back louvres to see if the missus is down in the garden, as she is sour on me drinking at any time, and especially early in the day. I open up a Fourex quick and lively and take a good long pull at it. Not that it does any good trying to hide it from her. She can smell it on me over the phone. Still, you can't very well let a bloke drink with the flies.

Reminds me of an old bloke up north who had a pub. He would never let anyone drink on his own in the bar. He reckoned it wasn't right, sort of like wardrobe drinking.

One day a stranger comes in and puts down just enough dough for one stubby. The old bloke looks hard at the money for a while, and then up at this bloke and says, "Aren't you drinking?" The bloke gets the message and dives past the death adder in his pocket and puts down enough for two!

By now the Irishman has started on about his eighth stubby which means that so far it has only seeped through to his fingertips. I down this drink steady-like, and I can feel it doing me the world of good straight away.

I get to wondering where the brewery gets all the good stuff that must be in it, and I get caught off guard because the Irishman says suddenly, "Those other two blokes never made it."

"Who are you talking about?" I say, coming in on this boots and all.

"Burke and Wills," he says with a cunning grin. I get the message and go and broach a couple more stubbies. It just shows how your mates will take advantage of you. Still it doesn't hurt to be kept on the ball, as there is always some smart aleck coming into the bar ready to have a go at you.

We have a couple more, then I say, "Listen, mate, I can't mark time with you all day. I've got work to do."

"Have another one with me, and then I'll give you a hand with the work," he says. I fall for this one (a man would fall for the three card trick), and then I've got to listen to all the bullshit he has got stored up in him after about a fortnight up in the hills talking to the bloody goannas. Still, I didn't want to work this morning. There's one thing about work; it will always be there to do tomorrow. It won't run away on you.

Then he starts telling me about a pet cockroach he has got up there which he has trained to answer commands. He reckons he is working on a theory that cockroaches have no ears and they hear through their feet, and proved this the other day when the cockroach refused to obey his command to run after he had pulled its legs off! You don't have to be mad to be a tin scratcher — but it helps.

Just then there's a bit of a diversion when a flash-looking Holden pulls up. The paint work is new, but you can tell she's a bomb by the queer noises coming from under the bonnet. Next thing a murri unwinds himself from behind the wheel, and another crawls out from the jump seat. They are obviously ringers from some cattle station.

They're not bad fellows on the whole, except in grog, and of course there's no distinction where the grog is concerned, because it brings out the meanness that's in any bloke's make-up.

These two come into the bar and get themselves perched on a high stool, giving the Irishman a quick look. One bloke starts working his lips ready to say something, like a blue-tongued lizard just finishing off a cane beetle.

"Boss." He finally gets it out. "You can change a cheque?"

"Yes, whose cheque?"

"Belong Laura Stashun," he says.

"OK. Where is it?"

So he digs down into his cunning kick, sometimes known as a fob pocket, and dredges up a battered bit of paper all creased up, and I'm wondering whether I will be able to read it when he does get it out. Finally he unpeels it enough to expose the front of it. I can see that it is just legible.

"Give these two boys a drink on me while they're waiting," chips in the Irishman. "Poor buggers are probably dying of thirst."

I whip the head off the first two stubbies I put my hand on — they don't mind what sort it is, as long as it's grog. When you see a murri getting fussy about what sort of beer he's drinking, you can say he's had just about enough — a white man too, for that matter.

When I get the cheque straightened out, I see that it's for about ninety bucks. I can see the company signature on the bottom of it, so I say, "You feller gotta sign this. You can sign your name?" He says yes, so I give him a biro to scratch away with. I can see that he has signed a few cheques before, from the way he keeps turning the cheque over back to front to see how his name's written in the pay column.

While he is so engaged, I turn on the other murrie and say, "You feller got a cheque too?" He says yes, and starts groping for it.

I'm awake to these blokes you see. He would have let me go in and open the safe, bring back the money for the other bloke, then he would have me go through the same rigmarole. Like when one bloke wants a packet of salted peanuts — you manage to get the tight-fitting lid off the tin and back on again, and the tin back in place on the shelf. Just when you have completed the deal, another bloke bobs up and says, "Me want one too."

I give this bloke a biro as well, and he starts mutilating the back of his cheque. When I look at the signatures I decide they will pass muster at the bank. The bank manager must reckon no-one could possibly forge the signatures as they resemble some of the pictures I've seen of fork lightning — in black of course.

By now the Irishman has got one of the blokes laughing about something, and it looks like they will set in for a steady session.

I take the cheques in and come back with the change. One is for ninety-two dollars and the other for ninety-seven dollars, and I forget which.

"Which one of you is the ninety-seven dollars?" They look blankly at me for a while and one bloke starts to open his mouth to claim it, but thinks better of it as he might be touching himself, so he clams up again. I have to walk back into the safe to dig out the cheques again to sort it out.

I finally give them their change, and tell them to hide some of it for after, as I know what happens when they get into town and get among their tribesmen up at the village. Within two days they will be flat broke, and trying to get a lift out of town back to the station.

They say they will put some away in "kitty", but they won't of course. The Australian abo is the only true socialist in the world. What he's got the rest of them have got.

Just then I sight a tourist coach coming down the hill laying a smokescreen of dust behind it. The coach pulls up with a flourish in front of the pub, with its trail of dust swirling up around it. Half of it gets swirled into the bar with a gust of wind, to settle on the counter.

One of the first to come into the bar is an old cheese who draws a finger through the dust on the counter and gives me a dirty look as much as to say, "Why don't you clean the joint up?" Little knowing that the dust there came with her lot.

Before I do anything, I take a quick run out the back to see if the missus is aware of the bus's arrival. I can see she is because she is starting to close up all the rooms — she knows they will be poking in and out of them like half-fed fowls looking for something to pick at.

I serve the old cheese with a whiskey and water, which she is obviously greatly in need of, and I can see she is eyeing-off the miserable two cents she gets as change. What the hell is she whinging about? I think. It's only a cent dearer than Melbourne, and they don't have to put up with bus tourists like we do.

Most of the others are milling about outside with cameras getting a photo of the old pub. This always amuses me; they've got the cost of a colour shot, plus the cost of getting it blown up to postcard size, along with about a seventy-five per cent chance of getting a dud picture. They could come into the bar and buy a professionally taken picture postcard of the joint for about a sixth of all that. I just can't figure them out.

By now there are a couple of diehard drinkers clamouring for a drink.

"Rum," says one bloke.

I dish out a snort, and say, "Any water?"

He shakes his head, as he can't talk, having already gobbled down a bit of genuine Nelson's blood — not that wishy-washy stuff they're used to down south. Now he knows what voltage it is, he takes it smoothly enough, but the way he starts to look furtively around, I figure out he must be an escapee from AA.

Another bloke says, "Stubby. Any sort." That's the sort of drinker I like.

A dame asks for a bottle of orange and two straws, and I'm a wake up to this lurk. She must have a mate outside she's going to share it with, being too bloody lousy to buy two bottles. This is the type you have to watch closely as they'll knock off the bottle when they go, and cash it somewhere else. As the price of the bottle up here is more than the profit in it, you've done your dough when they swipe the bottle. The non-returnable sorts are a bit of help this way. I hope they don't ever invent non-returnable tourists!

By now the Irishman has got the two murris laughing fit to kill them. That's a really good trait in a black fellow — he'll laugh loudly at any old joke, and when he throws his mouth open to roar with laughter, you can nearly count how many drinks he's had.

An old dame down the other end of the bar nudges my arm where I'm leaning on the bar, and says, "Aren't they quaint?"

"Who?"

"Those native boys."

"I don't know, missus. They look just the same as anyone else to me, only they're black." I can see this wasn't what she expected of me, believing I'd agree with any damn-fool thing she said, but this is one pub where the customer is not always right.

"Wasn't so long back when we used to boil those blokes down for ink, . . ." She whips round on me ready to do battle, but I cut her off, saying, " . . . That was before they invented biros of course."

"You're joking of course."

"No, missus," I say. "Fair dinkum. It wasn't so long back either when their grandfathers would have a feed of long pig any time they got the chance."

"What's long pig?"

"Roasted white man," I say, "but they liked fat Chinaman better — not so salty."

I can see she is starting to squirm a bit, and I don't mind this because if she moves out she will make room for another cash customer, as the bar is only about fifteen feet long, and bulging at the seams when you get a bus load of tourists in it, especially as the Irishman and the two murris are taking up the best part of about a third of the place, having been there first.

The bus driver comes in and asks for a soft drink, any sort, which I give him and don't take the money for. I reckon he has enough to put up with as it is, and I can see by his nose that he'd much sooner knock back a couple of VBs. They call them coach captains today, but this high-sounding title still doesn't give him the privilege of having a drink on the way.

I don't know how they can stand it — and put up with the mob as well.

After a while the blokes that have got a bit of a gutful start to move out, only the stayers still keeping a barrier position. Some of the weirdos start to move in, carefully at first, wondering whether I'm going to spring it on them for a couple of dollars cover charge like they do in those flash nightclubs in Sydney where you have to pay half the bloody licence fee for being on the premises.

A couple of them sneak in with their jeans just managing to defy the force of gravity. I know I won't get much out of these fellows, because if they did have a wallet in their hip-kicks with a bit of loot in it, the delicate balance would be upset, and the strides would come sliding down.

One bloke has to chuck his mane out of the way like a brumby stallion so he can see, but neither of them makes much of an effort to buy up big. I can see the wheels turning over, and I figure one bloke is going to think up the most awkward thing to get for the smallest price.

Sure enough he says, "Have you got a Bex powder?" So I reach over and slap a packet of Bex on the counter.

"Oh, I only wanted one."

"You better take the lot. You might get another headache tomorrow," but I can see he isn't too willing to be parted from his loot. "What am I going to do with a broken packet?" I say. "These blokes up here get proper headaches when they do, and they want a full packet to fix it."

Finally he can see I'm getting ready to put the packet back, so he says he'll take it.

I'm waiting now for the next act, as I know he's going to spring me for a glass of water so he can take the Bex. I can never subscribe to this method of taking a headache powder as I reckon you should chew it and keep the cure up where the pain is, and not wash it down as though you had a guts ache instead of a headache. But this joker sort of realises I'm not very well up on this public relations business, so he refrains from biting me for a glass of water. Him and his mate, who could be a deaf mute as I haven't heard a peep out of him, quietly mizzle off and later I see him taking his Bex with the dregs of someone's soft drink left on the verandah table.

I pass the visitors' book around, and they are all in on this as it's for free. I see a couple of way-out types writing and giggling about it, so I make a mental note to have a look at the book later, as sometimes they write stuff in there that wouldn't get into the Kings Cross Whisper.

Finally the bus dri . . . er, coach captain, starts to muster the herd, and he stands at the door of the bus helping these old dames up the steps who don't need help at all, as any one of them could hold their own with honours in a bargain sale at Myers Emporium.

What these bus blokes should have is a couple of dogs from those sheepdog trials at Sydney Exhibition. They reckon some of them are smart enough to get a blowfly into a pickle bottle, but they wouldn't have to be real smart to get this bunch of morons onto a bus.

Anyway, the bus bloke finally gets them all rounded up. He is helping one old codger up the steps, who looks like he's just about getting ready to chalk his last cue, and the only other one left is a bird that the Irishman has got hemmed in. He's making fabulous offers, he tells her, to get a young female cook — about her size — at his tin mine up at Mt Misery. Not many to cook for, either, he says. In fact only one . . . him. She takes a pierhead jump for the bus, just as the coach captain is about to blast off.

The bus takes off with the usual swirl of dust behind (pity the dust cloud doesn't go ahead of the blokes that make it), and things return to normal — or nearly so. The Irishman is telling the two murris what good fellows they are, and these two are telling the Irishman what a good fellow he is. Also what a good fellow the publican is, although they've only known me for about an hour.

I come back inside and start cleaning up the mess, and I say to Irish, "It wouldn't be so bad if it wasn't for the yaws."

He comes in on this and says, "What's yaws?"

"Fourex."

"OK," he grins, "you win. Get yourself one." So I broach a stubby and make a mid-course correction after being thrown a bit out of orbit by the last visitors.

The missus comes in and asks me if I want any food, but I say no, and she says, "At it again eh?" — and a man's been as flat as a tack in the bar since breakfast. So she asks the Irishman if he wants anything, but he says beer's food. I think the two boys might be a bit on the tooth, so I ask her if she has got a bit of spare goanna hindquarters there for them, but she gives me a dirty look and says, "No, but I have a proper meal ready if they want it."

So I say to the boys, "You fellers want tucker?" and they say, "Yes please." First time I heard anyone being polite in the bar for the last two hours. I tell the missus to bring in a plate of sandwiches, and we settle in for a bit of steady drinking.

Funny thing about this stuff; the more you have, the more you want, the quicker you want it. Don't know what the brewery puts in it to give it that more-ish taste. We carry on quietly for a while, and scoff the sandwiches between stubbies.

The Irishman is telling the two murris about some strange animal he's seen up in the hills. They are listening to him wide-eyed, not really believing the tale as they know perfectly well that there are no quinkens in the hills now, although there were plenty of these supernatural beasties there when their grandfathers were alive. But you never know . . . some of them may have survived. I am more interested in watching their reactions than listening to the

Irishman's story, as I know the weirdest animal in the hills up there is the Irishman — when he's not down at the Den.

He starts telling them about a rock python across the road so big he had to cut it up with the chainsaw into blocks and roll them out of the way so he could get the Land Rover past. He sights a big snake head on a neighbouring ridge and reckons it can't be the same snake. But it is, because as he starts to cut another block of tail off, it moves — the snake being that long that the head part is only just getting the message on the telex that he's getting carved up — and he sees the head coming down off the ridge after him. He's really got the boys in by this.

"By crikey, you fright eh?" says one boy.

"Too right I fright," says Irish. "I get the chainsaw ready to carve his head up when he gets down to me, but just then the bloody chainsaw run out of juice and stops."

"Hey, look out you feller!" the other murri says. "What you do then?"

"Well," the Irishman says, "nearly daylight then, so I wake up — and go and cook breakfast."

They both roar with laughter and, slapping him on the back, one fellow says, "By cri, you bin catch us proper that time."

The other boy pipes up and says, "Give us nuther drink Boss. You have one yourself too."

So I set the round up, and one for myself too as I'm not too proud to drink with a murri; after all, I've drunk with a few wharfies in my time. So we all have a drink, and the Irishman gurgles his down as though he's more convinced than ever that it's going out of fashion — that'd be his worst nightmare.

After this he is quiet for a while, which is a bad sign as it can only mean he's thinking up some more bastardry. Our attention is now diverted by another flash car that pulls up outside, gleaming as though she has just come out of the showroom. I can't tell what brand it is, but you can see it's an expensive job. Then she starts to disgorge, and about six people get out. You don't need a university degree to see that they've got class; probably sheep owners on holiday. So I'm sorely tempted to go inside and put a shirt on, but I think, no, what's good enough for one is good enough for the rest.

They amble towards the bar which is the first port of entry to any pub as far as I'm concerned. The big bloke who was driving is in the lead followed by what looks like Mum and the two girls. The two jokers could be the sons, but seem more like a couple of blokes in line for what's left out of the old man's estate after probate has been paid and the income tax bloke has laid his cleaver to one side.

"Is it all right for the ladies to come in?" says the big bloke.

"Certainly," I say. "Half my clientele are women." I

couldn't say "ladies", as the normal mob that frequents this joint would be offended if I called them that. They think it refers to those women who have no visible means of support.

They all pile quietly into the bar, and I clear a few empty stubbies away to give them a bit more elbow room, telling the boys to move along a bit to make way for cash customers.

The big bloke puts a rusty-looking note under one of the ashtrays and I think to myself, this is the sort of folding money I like to see around the place even if it does come from an overdraft. By the size of the motor car it'd be a sizeable overdraft too.

I smile at the old dame. I can see she has class and is a pretty good looker too; not like some of the old dears on the bus, who would have stopped a Centurion tank.

I give the bar a quick swipe down and empty the ashtrays while they sort of get settled in, picking the bar stools that don't look too rickety.

"What would you like to drink?" I say, and the boss bloke says, "Order up." He says he'll have a VB, the two jokers will have the same. The girls want Fourex, but the old lady decides on a sherry.

I whip out the stubbies and behead 'em, then the girls want a glass. I say I don't encourage it here, but seeing as they're strangers I'll stretch a point.

They are all eyeing-off the bottle collection, the snakeskins on the wall, and the native cat. (But I'm not going to tell that yarn again!)

The big bloke has folding up his six foot four onto a bar stool, so that brings him down to a level where I can talk to him, but the old lady is still standing up, despite the fact there are a couple of vacant stools. I guess she doesn't want to sit on them because she things the murris — or worse, the Irishman — may have been using them first. So I reach over and provide a nice new padded stool for her which I've got behind the bar.

She gives me a quiet little smile and regally parks her posterior on it. I give her the visitors' book to peruse, then go and put the change down in front of the old bloke.

"Would you care to join us in a drink?" he says, Now this is the sort of language I can really understand.

"Delighted."

"Perhaps those boys might care to join us as well."

I call out to Irish and say, "This gentleman wants to know if you'd like to have one on him."

"My very word I would," says the Irishman. The old bloke doesn't know what he's letting himself in for.

The murris don't say anything but I take it for granted they're going to have one. So I get the extra stubbies, and take what I reckon is a fair thing out of the old bloke's change which he leaves laying about on the counter like he doesn't own the stuff.

"Cheers!" we say. A violent slurping sound comes from the other end of the bar which we try not to notice. I can see the old duck isn't very keen on the sherry — she probably only had one to be in the swim. So far she's only lowered it by about two thicknesses of paint, so I get a bit confidential with her and say, "Don't you care for that brand?"

She says it's not the brand actually, it's just that she is not very partial to grog of any sort. She'd sooner settle for a good cup of tea any day.

"I'll fix that right away," I say. "What about the others?"

"Oh, the girls will be happy swilling beer." I take a quick look at the "girls" , and realise they are pretty nicely rounded for girls.

I go out into the kitchen and tell the missus that the old dame would like a cup of tea. This is right into her pannikin, as she'd sooner make two bob selling someone a cup of tea than make a quid selling that filthy grog.

"Send her out here," she says. So I go out and give her the high sign to come out of the bar and pilot her out to the kitchen. I don't know her name yet, but luckily I know Mum's name and that's good enough to start the introduction. The old girl supplies the other bits.

I leave them there, knowing they're going to lap each other up for another hour or so, which is a good thing as it'd be a pity to bust up a good drinking school like this threatens to be in the bar. When I get back the Irishman has got the old bloke bailed up at the end of the bar. Being a mastoid mangler par excellence, he's giving him the works.

Remembering I was going to look in the visitors' book to

see if the last crowd had left any nightcart material in it, I grab it. Straight away I see where she has drawn a line through something in the "Remarks" column, so I grab a biro and blot out the whole lot without reading it — better than any Minister for Customs could ever do. If it's not good enough for the old lady, it's not good enough for me. I've got a bit of a soft spot for her since she gave me that nice quiet little smile in the first place.

I also take the opportunity to read her name, and I can see they come from some station via Goondiwindi, so I reckon I was right. The whole bunch of them are riding on the old jumbuck's back. With the crowd that's on the old sheep's back, it's no wonder the pictures of those prize rams in the *Queensland Country Life* all look as though they have about six inches of their legs pushed into the ground.

I pass the visitors' book to the girls thinking they might like to make their dhobi mark in it. The first one gives me that same quiet little smile that Mama gave me, only her glance cuts off a bit sooner because this joker she's got with her is hanging round like an unsavoury smell and she doesn't want to offend him — yet.

I have a good look at this urger now, and his mate too. They look pretty well set-up young blokes, except it wouldn't hurt to have their ears lowered a bit. It must interfere with their hearing, having all that hair over them, but they always seem to hear well enough when somebody says, "Have another drink."

Old Woolbales says, "Have another drink." The Irishman pipes up and says it's his shout, but the old bloke says, "I insist." I don't mind this sort of stand-over tactics in the bar, so we line 'em up again.

I don't see the young fellows diving for their pockets, so I reckon they must both be slightly deformed; you know . . . arms too short. Still, they have the right sort of plum in their mouths to finally worm their way into the wool cheque, so I suppose they think they might as well let old Woolbales shout now just to get him used to the idea.

The other girl (she's nearly as good-looking as Mum, too) says how nicely behaved the two native boys are.

"I believe they're even intermarrying with the white girls now as well," she says.

The Irishman sticks his bib in and says, "That's nothing. There's a white woman up here married to a Scotchman."

While the girls are giggling about something in the visitors' book and are probably a bit crooked on me for scratching out what the hippie had written, I hear the radio come on with the racing commentary, so I go and shut it down.

"Don't you follow the horses?" says Old Woolbales.

"Yeah, but I mostly follow horses that follow horses." Then I tell him it's a bit hopeless up here, as you're flat out picking what horses are in the race let alone winners. I tell him that my son is at university studying Ancient History — I study it too . . . every time I get a racing paper. You don't get tomorrow's news today like they do in the city. You get yesterday's news in about a fortnight's time in the mail. I'll bet some of those doubles bookies grin when they write out their doubles sheets, because I'm sure some of the hairy goats they've got listed are already intended for the pet food assembly line, and are only there to trap the mugs.

I further state that they ought to get the RSPCA onto these jokers that kill good horses to feed mongrel Pekingese dogs; but I amend that by saying sometimes it's justified, especially when an odds-on favourite suffers a reversal of form. REVERSAL OF FORM me arse! They ought to put the hoop through the mill as well as the horse, and cut 'em both up for dog tucker. Except they should cut the jockey up into littler bits than the horse and spread him out with 1080 dingo baits.

The old bloke heartily agrees with me, as no doubt he's had a bit of a mauling in the past — maybe the not too-distant past at that.

I tell him about a bookie mate of mine (although a bookie's really got no mates), who I asked whether he was going to take some shares in an up-and-coming oil drilling company.

"No," he said. "Oil's too shifty for me."

Well, if the oil game is shiftier than the racing game, it ought to be outlawed along with nuclear weapons and women's libbers.

By now the Irishman has got into semi-holts with one of the hangers-on, and I can hear him saying, "Now listen here

Old Fellow," trying to get the right modulation into the voice but just not quite managing it. So I think it's time to take a hand, as I don't want a good school broken up. A man's got to live you know.

We line up another round and say to Woolbales that although the Irishman is pretty safe here, if I had a pub over in Belfast I'd frisk him to see if he had a couple of gelignite bombs on him before I let him into the joint.

I remark that over there they usually don't blow up pubs, unless they happen to get crook on the publican, but they must have a full-time job rebuilding post offices and cop shops. I reckon some of these bog trotters ought to be let loose in North Vietnam so they could just lead a normal life. They reckon now in the pubs in Ireland they don't sing out, "Time gentlemen, please", they just yell, "Which one of youse left this pram beside the bar here?" and this clears the joint in one and a half seconds flat.

The Irishman is going into a bit of a huddle with the bloke he was going to have a go at a while back (he's forgotten about that now), and he's busy telling him a yarn. He has manoeuvred this bloke out of his stool and has managed to get his own backside onto it. The girl is looking at him over her shoulder, studying him as though she's never seen anything like this in captivity before, and at that she could be right.

The two murris are talking quietly to each other, and drawing rings in the spilt beer on the counter. The old bloke has come out of his shell a bit and starts talking sheep. He tells me about a new process they're working on where they give the old jumbuck a pill. After a while you can just go and pull the wool off with your hands to save shearing, and thus get those highway robbers — the shearing gangs — off your back. This could be a good idea. They ought to get some of these retiring politicians to do the job as they're pretty good at pulling wool.

He talks a bit about industrial strife, then he must switch suddenly to conservation because he says all hawks ought to be shot — wedgetails and all other varieties. I don't want an argument, so to change the subject I ask him if he has any cattle as well as sheep, but he says, "No."

We have a good general grouse about everything, but I

can see the party is dying a bit, so I sneak my special matchbox into the counter near the girls while I wipe the bar down. This matchbox is a trick thing that goes off like a Big Ben alarm clock when you pick it up. You only have to leave it lying around long enough to catch somebody.

I'd like to catch one of the hangers-on, but I can see they're not smoking; probably been reading too many of these articles in the *Reader's Digest* about the dangers of drug taking. Either that or they've got a packet of pot cigarettes in their pocket which they're not game to produce, although they don't have the same glassy look in the eyes that these pot merchants usually have.

The only one smoking is one of the girls, so she has to be the sucker. I push the trick matchbox a bit closer to her next time I wipe the bar down, and I go up to listen to the Irishman.

He is holding a brief for the hippies, but as I know he's allergic to them it can only be an act.

"Of course," he says, "you can't blame them for the way they dress, look at the example they've got."

"What example?" says one bloke.

"From the first hippie."

The bloke asks who was the first hippie, and the Irishman says, "Why, old J.C. himself. Didn't he wear sandals and a beard and hand around the Cross?"

I decide there and then that I'm glad I never had to rear this bloke. I'm sure his own mother must've given him up as a hopeless case early in the piece.

Just then the girl who has been twiddling with the matchbox picks it up. It goes off with a shuddering rattle; she lets out a squeal and says, "Shit". She nearly falls backward off the stool, only being saved by the urger with her who wants any excuse to get his paws on her.

The Irishman roars with laughter and they all laugh except the old man who only grins as he says to her, "Mary, you could be a little more circumspect in your choice of words."

"The bloody thing went off in my hand," she says. "Thought I was getting an electric shock." She's got over her shock now and starts to laugh with the rest of them.

"Well, now that we've all come down to one common

level," says the Irishman, "what about having a drink with me?"

The old bloke, whose twenty-dollar bill has been reduced to a heap of shrapnel, rallies and says, "No, let me do this." He produces another rusty note and sticks it under the ashtray. I now decide he has a bigger overdraft than I first thought. Of course anyone can be free handed with dough they don't own, but he doesn't care whether he owns it or not, so I set the drinks up again.

The squeal that the girl let out has brought old Mama Woolbales back out of the hate session in the kitchen, as she could recognise her little chick-abidee's yelp; just like a mother seal can hear her own pup calling out amongst a thousand other pups, and sometimes wishes to Christ she couldn't.

I can see Mama bearing down on the scene, so I hurriedly wind up the clockwork in the matchbox and put it in the only vacant barrier position at the bar in the hope of catching her as well. I can see the girls and the old man are behind me in this. The old man is chewing his officer-type moustache with his bottom lip, mainly to stop grinning, but he can't fool the old vixen. I doubt he ever has been able, so why he thinks he can do it now I don't know.

She immediately smells a rat, and shies clear of the matchbox, just as though it had a label on it saying "Nuclear Warhead — Don't Touch". She wants to know what all the squeals and laughter were about. One girl says, "Nothing," and the other girl says, "Nothing."

My missus who has come in with her is awake straight away when she sees the matchbox, although it looks just like any other box of Redheads, except a bit more grubby — but she doesn't let on.

The old lady now says, "Well, when are we going to resume our tour?"

"Ah, don't go yet Mum, we're just starting to enjoy it here." I can see old Woolbales has just about got enough turps into him to not give a damn whether the cow calves or breaks its neck.

The Irishman sidles up to the old dear, puts his arm round her shoulders and starts to tell her how it's not often we have such a handsome aristocratic lady like her around the place, and the girls are only young once. It's a pity to spoil their fun.

The old lady is looking hard at the Irishman and playing it cool, as she doesn't like to make any sudden moves in case she startles a flock of bats out of his beard. You can see by the steady look she gives him that she has got his measure, and this blarney stuff, which is only the Irish word for bullshit, doesn't get her in.

When I look again at her I reckon her dear old grandmother herself might have come from Country Cork anyway, and that's where they invented this hoo yah, so it doesn't cut much ice with her. Besides, I know that the Irishman comes from County Armagh. He wouldn't have been able to save the fare over there to take a trip down to Blarney Castle, although it's only about as far as from here to Laura.

How he ever got the fare to come to Australia has got me buggered, as they are all a bit short over in the Emerald Isle. The chances are that he fell foul of the London coppers, and the bloke on the bench at the Old Bailey explained to him the difference between transport and transportation.

However, I can see his efforts are softening the old girl up a bit — there's none of them that won't fall for this blarney stuff if you lay it on with a trowel — and I feel a bit relieved as I thought she was going to bust up a good sort of a session.

I can see my missus' antennae wiggling as she turns on her instant breathalyser. I don't know what the coppers want all these bags and chemcial things for when all they'd have to do would be to take her on the rounds with them. She can tell from thirty feet away how many drinks a bloke has had, and where. But not who with. Even the best machines have their limits. Just the same she whinges if we don't collect 500 bucks a day, and I haven't got half that yet. It looks like a hard day's night ahead of me and a man would never do the distance without a bit of steam in him.

The other girl pipes up and says? "Mum, who was the first beatnik?" and to this Mary says, "You can't tell that story Anne. Not to Mum." But she has enough of what they call Dutch courage to go ahead with it anyway. When it's finished the old lady calls us a bunch of heathens and heretics, but I think I can see the suspicion of a grin on her dial. My missus backs her up and says we all ought to be ashamed of ourselves.

She comes from a place called Warwick on the Downs where they have nearly as many churches as pubs, which I reckon is a sort of imbalance in any community. They should sack the town planner and get a more liberal-minded bloke in as the architect. After all, that works out at about one sin doctor per pub, and when they're in strength like that there's the risk they might convert a few of my sort.

This is a process that could snowball and the next thing you know we'd have to shut down half the pubs. Trade would all go to these newfangled tavern joints and bistros, which is the same thing only worse, because you have to associate with a lower type of customer. Some of these new joints have so much chrome and glass and stuff like modernistic sculpture that they wouldn't let a self-respecting murri in, let alone the Irishman.

That way a man could die of dehydration. Still, we shouldn't get too pessimistic as long as we still have the old Den. It may turn out to be the last stronghold of the genuine old stubby drinker.

I can see the murris are making a bit of sign talk for me to come down their end of the bar.

"We gotta go now," says one bloke.

"OK. What you wanta take with you?"

"Botla wine. No. Make it two."

I don't like this much, so I say, "I think you better only take one. You feller get too drunk, you get in trouble." So I wrap up one bottle of port for them. "That will be enough to get you to town. You can get some more there if you want it." One bloke puts his roll on the counter and I take what is a reasonable amount out of it.

I hear a vehicle pull up in front, coming from the Bloomfield way but I don't take much notice of it. The boys want another bottle of wine, but I reckon they've had a fair innings, so I knock them back.

"You blokes want to look out. Otherwise you'll get in trouble with the Sergeant."

"We doan fright for Chargent," says one boy, and damn me if the Sergeant and the Constable don't come walking into the pub. They must've gone down to Bloomfield before daylight and I missed them.

The Sergeant forces his way into the bar, bulging the door frame as he enters, closely attended by his Constable. He comes and stands over the now visibly shaken murri.

"Who's not frightened of the Sergeant?"

"We not talk properly that time Chargent. We jokin', that's all."

"Just as well."

The boys are trying to make a move to get out, but the other copper has got them hemmed in a bit. "What you got in that bottle, eh?"

"Wine, That's all," he says. "I take it to my missus."

"I can imagine how much your missus will get out of it. Probably a hit over the head with the empty bottle. Who is the driver?"

"Me", says one fellow.

"I don't know whether to let you fellows drive like you are." He turns to me and says, "How much have they had to drink?"

"Not much," I say. "And they've had a bit of tucker too. They'll be OK unless a bloodwood tree jumps out in the middle of the road in front of them." Which has happened to blokes round here several times, including me, but I don't tell him that.

"Well, you fellows just watch what you're doing on the way in," says the Sergeant. "And don't think I won't be behind you, because I will be. Keep that wine for when you get to town. I'll call into the village on the way to see if you've still got it. Now get going." He turns to me and orders a couple of stubbies.

The boys depart and the Irishman sings out goodbye to them. The girls wave and the murris wave back, but their hearts aren't in it now.

"They'll be all right," I say to the Sergeant. "You've frightened half the grog out of them anyway." I see the Constable fingering the matchbox and I think any time now he's going to pick it up, but he doesn't. The girls were getting themselves all worked up waiting for him to come in on the matchbox.

Then I see that one boy has left his money behind. The

coppers suggest taking it in to him, but I say no. The murris have plenty between them, and this way they'll have a bit to fall back on. If they have the lot now the other blokes in town will have it all by tomorrow night.

So I put it in an envelope, and as I don't know which bloke it belongs to, I draw a goanna on the front of the envelope and put it on the shelf.

"If you see them, tell them the dough is here, otherwise they might think they lost it on the way, or their mates at the village have knocked it off."

I can hear the Irishman "chewing his cud" over something, mainly I suppose because he thinks the coppers hunted the two boys out of the bar. They were going anyway, only he doesn't know this. I go down to see what he's bitching about to the old bloke, and that's what it is. I tell him the coppers have a job to do whether they like it or not.

"The Sergeant's all right in his place."

"Yeah," says the Irishman. "But they haven't dug it yet."

The girls sight a book on the shelf which has a "banned" title on it. They want to see it, but I make out that I don't want to give it to them as it's not the sort of publication you should even handle without washing your hands afterwards in disinfectant.

After a bit more palaver I grudgingly give it to Anne — the one that's got a bit of a crease down her forehead, as though she mightn't be getting her fair share of the good things in life. I look at the bloke with her and wonder if he's really pulling his weight.

She pounces on the book and opens it up. It's not a book at all, only a hideout for a bloody great snake that springs out into the air as soon as you open the book. She lets out a squeal and nearly falls arse over head off the stool, but is saved by the hanger-on who holds the clinch about five seconds longer than need be, this being the first time I've seen him doing anything constructive.

She is a bit more refined than the other one because she doesn't say shit, but maybe that's only because the coppers are still there. They roar with laughter and so does the Irishman and old Woolbales who can't contain himself this time. The squeal and the laughter bring the old mother duck back, and she asks what's going on now, but the girls are laughing too much to tell her. Then she sights the rubber snake on the bar floor and lets out a yelp which only increases the laughter.

She can see that she's fighting a losing battle, so retires to the safety of the car, as my missus has got work to do. It's just was well somebody does a bit around the place.

Things settle down a bit after this, and old Woolbales asks the coppers to have a drink, but they say no, they have work to do, for which I am pleased as it's only a matter of time before the Irishman will start making cracks at them, which can be very embarrassing . . . not for the coppers, but for me.

So the coppers take off and everyone says goodbye except the Irishman, who only makes rude gestures which luckily the Law doesn't see. I warn him about a bloke getting fined 100 dollars the other day for the same thing. He says it'd be worth every penny of it.

Old Woolbales unwinds himself from the stool, and he's got enough nous to say, "Where is it?" Not "Have you got a toilet here?" The two young fellows follow him, which is a fatal move, because it leaves the two girls wide open to the Irishman. It's no time before he's got his arms round both of them at once, and they are pleasantly thrilled to be rubbing up against such a dangerous-looking animal only to find that it's quite docile.

I can hear the footsteps coming back, so I give the Irishman the nod and he breaks the clinch just in time. They ask him what he does for a living and he says he's a tin scratcher. I can see they are puzzling this one out, and they think he must be part of a musical outfit like the steel bands they have over in the Caribbean, so I come in and explain it to them. A tin scratcher is a tin miner who works on his own, and I dump a big slug on the bar, which is a nugget of tin of about seventy per cent purity. They try to lift it but can't. They think I must have switched on a magnet or something to hold it down, but it's only the weight of it which does this. One of the boys shows how strong he is and after a couple of goes, picks it up one handed. I see him rubbing his wrist afterwards.

The party is dragging a bit now, so I say I'm going to

break a longstanding rule and shout. Irish says it's his go, and Woolbales says it's his party, and I leave them arguing the point while I get the drinks. However I can see if we don't get some new blood into the deal shortly, it's going to fold up. Just then a local bloke who owns a small cattle station comes along, driving an old bull and a couple of bull stags ahead of him. He leaves the murri with him to take the beasts along, and gets off his horse and heads for the bar.

He goes straight round to the speakeasy at the end. We used to reserve this for the murris but they drink in the bar now. The way they're going, before long we'll have to get the Government to set up a Department of White Man Affairs to look after our interests. The murris outnumber us about ten to one in the Peninsula.

I dish out a rum for the cattle bloke, as I don't have to ask him what he wants.

"Have a drink with me," he says to the bar.

"No," says Woolbales, "this is mine." So they all say "Cheers", and Woolbales wants to know what the cattle bloke's doing with the beasts. He says he's sending them away on the road train next week to the meatworks.

I chip in and say that the bulls are really going on one of these package tours you read about . . . over to the States, packaged up in seven pound tins, which makes him grin a bit.

"I don't know how those Yanks can come at this bull meat. They won't even use it for dog tucker on the stations."

Woolbales says it's the same in the sheep game. "Some of the stuff they put in tins, it's got me how anybody can eat the tack."

He gets onto export of live sheep and the troubles attached to it, what with the graziers trying to push them out of the country to get a quid and the unions trying to push them back into the country just to be bloody difficult. The Middle-east market is screaming for more live mutton, only they're demanding that the sheep must be delivered complete with testicles. I say this is only a lurk to get more weight, and has got nothing to do with religion at all.

Then we get onto 1080 baiting, and how the dingo population has been reduced, and old Woolbales says it kills a few other things too. I say, "Yes, apparently it kills a few crows and wedgetails and other birds." This starts him off again talking about hawks — but I won't buy into politics. A publican has to steer a middle course, otherwise he finds half his cutomers drinking at the opposition pubs.

Next thing we hear the horn of the car blowing and we all know it's not Gabriel's horn, but the message is equally clear and insistent. So the party reluctantly stretches itself amid a scraping of bar stools, and the old bloke says, "Well, it's time we got going," and I agree with him — reluctantly, because not only are they free with the quid, but pleasant company as well.

We shake hands all round and the Irishman is determined to kiss the girls which he finally manages to do though the girls aren't really keen on it because it's like sticking their moosh into an old busted saddle with the stuffing bulging out everywhere through the counter-lining. Then he shakes hands with the two young fellows as well — I think for a moment he is going to kiss them too, but it appears they are not that way inclined.

The old bloke asks for a half-dozen to take with them for the road and I quickly wrap these up. They all troop out of the joint, the girls walking backwards and waving, "See you again sometime . . . we hope."

I sing out to old Woolbales he's left his change on the counter, though it's only the bare bones of the twenty dollar bill.

"Let the tail go with the horns," he says. "You fellows have another one on me," which is damned decent of him. You can always tell a real aristocrat. They get in this big car which I never did figure out the make of, and whirl her round and away at about ten knots faster than what they came in, laying a pollution trail like a jet liner.

2

The Irishman says what about we have one, so we hook into the dregs of old Woolbale's dough. We get big-hearted and ask the cattle bloke to have one too, and he doesn't need any urging.

I start to straighten the place up a bit and get into shifting a few empty stubbies which have been gaining on us. In the process I get caught with the trick matchbox myself, and say, "Bugger the thing." After getting all the empties into spare cartons and cleaning the bar down, I say to the Irishman, "What about giving me a hand?"

So he comes in, carries all the empties out to the right place, and sweeps the bar out saying, "Look out, dorg." The cattleman's dog gives him an injured look and crawls away under the couch on the verandah where it's harder to get at him.

I've still got to dispose of the empties later, which is a job a man wouldn't have to do if they'd only invent a stubby like an icecream cone so that the customers could eat the bottle after they've drunk the grog. You wouldn't find so much "litterbuggery" going on, though you'd still have some mug chucking bits over his shoulder and saying, "I don't like necks."

An edible bottle would come in handy up here. We all know how to dispose of the grog, but not what it comes in. They could have different flavours in the edible bottle, like cornbeef, steak 'n' onions and fish 'n' chips, and do away with the present labels, which wouldn't matter much as it all tastes as though it came out of the same vat anyway, especially after about the third stubby. They could have filet mignon and pate de foie gras for the poofters that try to make out that they're a cut above you and me. They could cater for the murris by having a few stubbies impregnated with extract of witchetty grub or casseroled goanna tail, though they don't go for this tack now like they used to.

This would dispose of the litter problem as far as stubbies are concerned, and there'd be no washing up of glasses, but I suppose some bastard would always want a knife and fork to eat his stubby with, and a man would be back to taws with the washing up.

Well, the cattle bloke has another couple of OP rums, then he forks his horse and sets off. The Irishman, who is by now in a semi-liquid state, goes out to the verandah and ploughs into the Couch of Repentance there. Just then the missus calls out to me to come and shoot a hawk that's trying to get a feed of unbarbecued chicken.

I grab the old Greener gaspipe and put a Number Seven shot in it, because it's no use me trying to do any fancy shooting in the state I'm in. I blast away at him, and he flies off a bit wobbly, slow and erratic-like. He's not going to break any track records with the weight of lead he's carrying. Never a dull moment.

I come back into the bar and do a bit of cleaning up; I can see the couch has thrown the Irishman (apparently never followed the hounds in County Armagh), but he's still got one leg in the stirrup. However he's just as happy on the floor as anywhere else because it reminds him of home.

I take a good look at him and decide that if ever I get stuck for a quid, I'll put him in a sideshow, and follow the show circuit — but I'm not sure what to bill him as. Maybe it would be all right to advertise him as the "Wild Man from the Peninsula" and have him in a good solid steel cage to make out how dangerous he is. Then put a trace chain round his neck for good measure and have him eating raw meat; though with the present price of T-bone, the venture mightn't turn out economic. I know he wouldn't eat tripe as he already has a gutful of that from listening to political speeches on the radio. Maybe I could feed him on goanna tail if I could only get onto a good source of supply.

They call goanna tail "overland trout", because it tastes so much like fish, but being a Catholic, the chances are that the bastard would only eat it on Friday and leave me to nut out a cheap menu for the other six days of the week. I know how expensive the liquid side of his diet is going to be, so a man would have to watch the budget pretty closely if he were going to get anything out of it.

I know he couldn't go all day in the show without talking, so I'd have to get him to brush up on his native tongue whatever the hell that is, whether it's Gaelic or Celtic or Erse (which sounds like a dead language to me). If he mixed the three of them up together, he could gabble away all day and nobody'd have a bloody clue what he was talking about. He could abuse hell out of the mugs that throw loaded peanuts into the cage without getting into trouble with the coppers. There are not as many Irish coppers around these days like there used to be to recognise some of the home-grown words.

It's nice to have time to think about these things when there are no customers for the moment, and the Irishman is sleeping off his first session of grog and making noises like a small case-mill cutting up dry pine for pineapple cases.

I have spoken too soon, as I can see at any moment he's going to come up for air. I sort of dread this, as I have no-one else here at the moment to share him with and will have to bear the full brunt of him when he comes on deck.

Sure enough he gets up and stretches himself and asks what time it is, and I answer, "Daytime" — just to get him on the ball. I tell him he'd better go out to the bathroom to sharpen himself up because the bus will be here soon with another bunch of travellers. I don't want them to think we sleep all bloody day like flying foxes, and go round all night squealing and knocking mangoes down on the roof.

So he goes out to the bathroom, and comes back looking a new man and he says, "VB. Are you going to have one?"

And I say, "No, I've seen the light," and I go to the fridge and accidently come back with two stubbies which is an automatic reflex. I really didn't intend to.

"Well," he says, "you may as well have one now you've brought it out," and I behead them, telling him that I'm quarter Irish anyway. Maybe that's how I can put up with him. Then I tell him a bit more about my ancestry which is something like one of those Heinz dogs — though not as bad, as my ancestors came from England, Ireland, Scotland and Wales, in that order. With such a mixture of blood a man would never get into the stud book.

He contends that I've listed them wrong though and that I should put the Scots section last, but I say no, because the Welshmen still live in rock shelters with the cracks plugged up with cowpads. I speculate about whether they have a Department of Abo Affairs over there to look after them, and he admits that some of the Irish tribes are just as bad. It's crook in wintertime when you have to take the bloody pigs in as well. If you don't look out the pigs take over and you're flat out holding a barrier position yourself.

But, he says, not nearly as bad as the Scotsmen, because you have to put up with the bagpipes as well, which is the final straw.

Then I tell him that I don't go much on the pommies either for that matter because I am in direct line of descent from old Red Robbie the Norman warlord who came over and beat the arse off them before they were even called pommies. On the maternal side I'm from Captain Cook, I tell him. One of the main reasons why I came to live at the Lion's Den was because Joe Banks gave Cook a sketch map of the area with a ring around one spot marked "Fuitable fite for fettlement", which as near as I could figure out was just about where the old Den stands today. Jimmy Cook handed the map down through the various families till it came into my possession, and that decided me.

The Irishman chews this over for a while, but he can't go one better for the moment, as the grog hasn't started to work in him properly yet.

Just then I see the dust trail of a bus coming down the hill. I sweep the Irishman and his beer along to one end of the counter to make room for possible cash customers. Although ordinary bus passengers don't usually spend up big — unlike the coach tours — you never know.

I put my half-finished stubby under the counter because I know my better half will come into the bar to give me a hand with the bus tribe. They always want a heap of soft drinks and straws and bloody chocolates and things which just shouldn't be allowed in a public bar anyway — but we have to keep them because it's nineteen hard miles to the nearest corner shop.

This bus comes in nice and steady with very little dust cloud dragging behind, because it's the driver who owns this one and it's him who has to buy the new brake linings — not like the other bloke; but then he's only a bus driver, and the other bloke's a coach captain.

He pulls up and then starts backing right in under the mango trees, to get as close as possible so we don't have to carry the cargo too far. The crowd piles out of the bus door and into the bar, and for ten minutes Mum and I are as busy as a one-armed paperhanger with the itch, but they finally settle down a bit. One bloke asks if he can get accommodation. I say he can, and Mum says he can go in room two. I show him where it is along the front verandah, and tell him there are two beds in it.

"Which bed?" he says.

"Take you pick. There's no other bloke in there, so you won't be able to argue with him."

I take another look at him and see that he'd never get into the finals in a Mr World competition. He has a long, lean-looking face that you could easily hang a bridle on by mistake on a foggy morning, and a queer sort of look in his eyes, and I wonder what form his insanity is going to take. It's marvellous how you can pick 'em. He takes up a position down near the Irishman who is studying him like a geological specimen, not saying anything.

There's another bloke down the other end of the bar ripping stubbies into himself as fast as he can, as if he's thinking the bus might go before he's got a chance to get properly refuelled. He keeps letting out big burps between guzzles as though he came from the Belchin' Congo. The Irishman says to me on the side that if they could only get him down near Bass Strait, they could tap him as a source of natural gas; and I think this bloke must have heard a bit of this because he gives Irish a beady-eyed stare, but doesn't comment.

Just then the Irishman lets out a roar, there's a scuffle and a yelp and he says, "Get out you mongrel bastard," and the Belchin' Congo bloke sings out, "Hey, *hey*, don't kick a dog!"

"If you're such a dog lover, sport, take him down your end and let him cock his leg on you for a change," says the Irishman, which shuts the other bloke up, as this is a good enough excuse any day of the week to kick a dog in the ribs.

This closes the incident, but I can see the Irishman is planning revenge, as these bog trotters are nearly as good as the Mafia or a bunch of Chimbus in this "pay back" business.

The burp artist is not really matey with me either, as he can see the suspicion of a grin on my face over the dog incident. The next thing the Irishman slides out of the bar, and shortly afterwards comes back into the bar through another door, pushes up past this bloke and asks me for a box of matches. I know there's some bastardry afoot as he could have just as easily got them up the other end of the bar.

Then he says, "Sorry, mate," as he accidentally bumps this bloke going out. I can see the manoeuvre now, because he has hung a rubber snake on this character's belt, with a bent pin which is in it for just this purpose. The snake looks more real than the genuine article, and it wriggles a bit as the bloke moves.

Two teenagers come in to get soft drinks; they see the snake and sidle along the bar a bit away from this bloke as though he had BO bad. He gives them a mean look and swamps some more beer. Irish is busy down the other end talking to Horseface who seems to be happy to sort of be accepted as one of the mob so early in the piece. As I said before, the Irishman can be mates with anybody . . . nearly.

The mob outside has got onto the snake by now and there is a bit of giggling going on. Old Belchin' Congo gives a good solid belch in their direction, catches sight of the snake out of the corner of his eye, gives a gasp and a jump at the same time, and the snake falls on the bar floor still wriggling. He is scared to death of it, until one of the teenagers picks it up and puts it on her mate's head, who lets out a squeal. The bloke now knows it's phoney, but he doesn't know who to attack over it, as he's not sure it's the Irishman's doing. He can't very well go for the two girls, so he just glowers at everyone. He suspects I know a bit more than I should about the deal, given the ringside seat that I've got.

When I say, "Would you like another beer, sir?" he gets up real cranky and says, "Stick the beer up your arse," and stamps out of the bar, and the Irishman says, "Goodbye, sport."

I told you a while ago that I was quarter Irish, and it's just as well that quarter of me was away on long service leave at the time. Anyhow old Sourguts gets into the bus and a buzz of conversation starts up again. I ask Horseface if he has unloaded his gear, and of course he hasn't and runs out madly to get it. You have to wet nurse these bloody types.

The bus man has unloaded the next week's grog and Mum is out there doing the tally clerking. Then the busman and me and Irish hook into it and get it into the spirit room before some light-fingered type can knock a carton off.

The bus man bloke comes into the bar. He is known as Barefoot Bill because he doesn't wear boots or shoes any time. He says he gets a better "feel" of the bus with no boots on, only sometimes after a long, hard pull, you have a bit faster ride down the other side because the brake pedal gets too bloody hot for him to put his foot on it. He signs his name on the back of the bus with two dirty big black footprints. I sometimes wonder if he signs his cheques the same way, but I'll probably never know as I don't get any cheques off him . . . he only gets them off me. He reckons now he's gone long enough all day without a grog, so he has one too. Reckons the bus knows its way in from here anyway.

An old tourist lady comes in and starts talking about the old pub. I can tell from the dialect she's using she comes from Yorkshuh, and she says that the first time she heard about our old pub she was in Loondin, and she was determined to visit it. I say it is a long way to come just to see an old pub, and, "Surely you must have some old pubs nearer home worse than this one." She says they have put nobody lives in them, and I say a bloody good job too, if they are worse than this. She smiles and says, "They are mostly bombed-out ones from the war, which they didn't bother to rebuild."

"This joint has to stand up to treatment as bad as the London Blitz all the time," I say, "and it's still hanging together; but only just."

Then the old dear signs the visitors' book, and I tell her that when the Queen came to Cooktown, she was going to come to the Lion's Den, but they weren't sure whether the Rolls Royce would be good enough to pull up the Black Mountain. I'd have had to go out there an pull it up with the Jap four-wheel drive that I've got. We decided that it wouldn't be right for a Jap vehicle to go ahead of the Queen's limousine, so we had to call the deal off.

She especially wanted to see the place, I tell her, because her great-great-grandma was a good pal of Joe Banks, only she called him Sir Joseph. Then I tell her he was the bloke that picked the spot where they put in the first Australian datum peg — survey marker — and that this pub was built round it.

The tourist lady wants to see the peg, but I say the bloody white ants turned it into dust long ago. They'd have the pub too, only for all those blokes that are too bloody lazy to walk round to the toilet at night. They haven't bred a strain of white ant yet which can develop immunity to uric acid.

Then she says what a pity the Queen couldn't make it, as I could then put up a sign to say that the pub was under Royal patronage. I tell her not to worry about that, as the joint is already under Royal patronage. I have the Irishman here at the moment and he is one of the uncrowned kings of Ireland, having descended direct from a bloke named Brian Boru (which sounds more like an Aboriginal from Arnhem Land than an Irish king).

I pull the Irishman in on the deal and introduce them. I call him quietly "Your Majesty", and the old dear gives me a quick look to see if I am fair dinkum or not. I'm not grinning, so she thinks there might be something in it after all, but by the suspicious way she's looking at him, I think she is more ready to belive he's one of the IRA or a Sinn Feiner, and he could be both for all I know.

I have to go and serve a couple more drinks here and there, and make a few observations to the bussy, but out of the corner of my ears I can hear this bog-trotting bastard tell such outrageous hogwash to the old girl that I feel ashamed for introducing her to him.

Not only is the bastard a stranger to the truth, but he doesn't even live in the same suburb. I feel like crawling into a hole and pulling it in after me, because she's such an old dear. I've never heard so much sophistry, mendacity, cant and straight out distortion of the truth in my life.

I know the bus is going to go before long, so I decide to go down and bust into the conversation to give the old girl a bit better impression of the place before her departure. So the first time the Irishman draws breath I chip in and tell her a bit more about the original datum peg that Joe Banks stuck in.

I tell her that because the white ants kept eating out the wood pegs which they used to replace the original peg with, they got a team of surveyors up and ran a traverse from this peg down to the bridge at the Little Annan. They drilled a hole in the granite rocks there, and drove a brass plug into it so the white ants couldn't eat it out, and made it the State datum peg. All the rest of the surveys in the State were tied in with it.

I tell her they ran another traverse from the new peg into Cooktown, where young Jimmy Cook had already driven a peg years ago, and proved he'd been spot on. But those bludgers in New South Wales won't accept this as a datum point because they say young Cook wasn't an authorised surveyor. I say this is only straight out interstate jealousy, but they will persist in using Sydney Observatory as the State datum, and we all know that it's not as accurate as Cook's position.

When you see all these ships piling up in the Great Barrier Reef, you know that they are mostly New South Wales ships, not Queensland ones, because we bear a bit of allegiance to the old Navigator. We take all our bearings off Cook's monument in Cooktown, which is right on top of the Lowmoor iron peg which he put in. Joe Banks stubbed his toe on it just after Cook drove it and said, "Effit," and Cook said, "What's that?" Banks picked himself up quickly and said, "It's a fine effort," because he knew Cook wouldn't wear those four letter words at any price.

"Well, come on you good people," says the bus driver, "we must get going."

I can see old Sourguts in the bus, and he is sourfaced as well. The charge that he got in him when he first came in has started to wear off a bit with all the delay, but he can't come in to top it up again, because he burnt his boats when he told me what to do with my beer.

Well, they all quietly mill out of the joint, only Horseface remaining because he's got a barrier position at the bar, and he's going to stick to it. I start to give the Irishman a piece of my mind about how he misled the old dear and brought discredit on the pub . . .

"You dirrrty, low-down, lying, bog-trotting, Irish bas . . ." and I cut off in mid-sentence and the Irishman cuts off in mid-breath, because we hear the old dear talking to someone just outside the bar.

She's telling this person how entertaining it has been, and how she has been talking to two boys in the bar — although the chappie behind the bar couldn't very well be classed as a boy. I think to myself, "Don't trust me too far just the same." She says how interesting it was, but they had such *vivid* imaginations.

I hear the Voice of Prophesy, and I say to the Irishman, "The Voice of Prophesy tells me this old dragon has been in front of us all the way."

The Irishman is caught speechless for a moment and this is not like him at all at all. We hear the old girl telling this other party that it's a pity we couldn't introduce a wee modicum of truth into our yarns, but it was still interesting as it proved how fertile the imagination of man can be. Her voice fades away as she walks to the bus.

The Irishman just starts to get his hot back and he starts off, low at first.

"The hag, the crone, the harridan, the old trout, the sneakin' old bitch! Takin' us in like that, it fairly shakes me faith in human nature," he says. "Here's me thinking what a good story I'm giving her . . . it just goes to show. You can never trust a bloody pommy."

Well, they finally herd 'em all into the bus and the bus driver starts up the diesel engine. Before he can get away, the exhaust, which is pointing straight at the bar, blows a few cubic yards of carbon monoxide into the bar. I have to get out for a while afterwards to let the pollution level subside a bit.

A good gust of wind reduces the fog until we can just see, so I go back in and take up the croupier's position. The Irishman comes back in and the game goes on.

3

We have another stubby, as it's been quite a while between drinks with all the upheaval attached to getting the bus in and out, talking and playing mean tricks on the travellers, etc. The Irishman says he wants a gallon of plonk to take with him when he goes (if he goes), and I say we should start to get used to this new crazy system of weights and measures and start practising with metric madness right now.

I want to get used to it anyway because a man might be touching himself if he's not all clued up on it.

"OK," says the Irishman, "I want a metre of port."

"What you mean is a litre of port."

He chews this over for about two seconds and says, "No, buggerit. Make it a metre. I like a long drink." You just can't win.

I get a gallon jar of steam out of the spirit room and he goes and puts it in the Land Rover, otherwise he might forget it if he does happen to go, which is doubtful. I mention that I'm getting a bit short of jars, and if he sees any of those Bloomfield types, to tell them to bring back a few empties as they drink the stuff in quantity down there. There are so many empties strewn around they call the place "the Plain of Jars".

I ask Horseface to sign the guest register seeing as he's staying here. Usually this way you can find out a bloke's name without him knowing you're a sticky beak. He signs it, but it looks like about three inches off the graphpaper mark made by the Cooktown Post Office barograph during a severe cyclone, so I'm no bloody wiser.

I'm still thinking of him as Horseface. I tell the Irishman this and say that he looks something like Baghdad Note but he says no, Bunratty Castle, which is sticking up for his own bailiwick of course. He never did like those New Zealanders very much and he reckons there should be a strict quarantine on all horses into Australia just before the Melbourne Cup, to give the local boys a chance to win it. The Cup's on our mind at the moment, of course, it only being a few days away.

This mention of Bunratty Castle starts the Irishman talking about the bogs of Ireland. There's very little else to talk about over there as it's about ninety per cent bog anyway. The only solid land is where the pommies have got a foothold up in the north of Ireland which is where my quarter share of the bastards come from, but I don't let on about this. I know these tin miners always have a bit of gelignite around to loosen up the dirt in the face if the nozzle is not cutting too good.

I say the pommies must be having it tough up there, what with a mob of bloody heathens on their southern boundary, and a bunch of bagpipe-squeezing heretics across the canal at their backs, and only rubber bullets to shoot with because of excessive union demands at Mount Isa making the price of lead prohibitive. He says it's just as bad only a lot worse (which is typical Irish talk) for the Irishmen, because despite the price of lead being so high — if they could buy it — they couldn't get a decent stockpile together because it'd only sink down into the bogs. Besides, if they did get the upper hand and banished the Anglo-Saxon Tyrant from their shores, who the bloody hell would they have left to fight then?

This would mean that they would have to start fighting amongst themselves, and then there'd be real slaughter. He reckoned that if he was a strong patriot, which he is not, he'd start collecting one cent pieces to send over to the rebels.

I say the one cent pieces wouldn't finance much. He says no, but they fit a twelve-bore shotgun real nice. He reckons that is all one cent pieces are good for, as even the bloody kids can't be bothered picking them up off the ground. I agree with him because I don't deal in the things at all, just taking the change in round figures.

All this time, Horseface hasn't come in on anythying at all, though he's listening real hard. I can almost see one of his ears cocked a bit forward and the other cocked a bit back like a bloody rogue horse getting ready to kick your guts out while you're sneaking up on him with a bridle. I decide he'll bear watching. So far I haven't figured out what form of insanity this bloke subscribes to, but I know it's going to be something.

The Irishman tries to get a bit friendly with Horseface, but it's bloody hard. Just like when I go into Cooktown now and then and want to have a few grogs and I've got my "hand brake" with me.

Anyhow Irish asks him to have another drink to which this joker readily agrees, as this appears to be his main function in life. Irish slaps him on the shoulder, then pulls his hand back sharply to inspect it, just as though he'd been stung by a Scots thistle, but it was only a nagoora burr stuck in this bloke's shirt.

I can see the Irishman is very curious to sound this bloke out to see where he comes from. He's got a terrible dawning suspicion that he could be a Scotsman, or perhaps a Welshman — which isn't quite so bad — or possibly a Manxman which is the fifth tribe in the Ununited Kingdom. The sixth is the Channel Islanders, but you don't count them as they're just blown-away Frenchmen. The neighbouring French peasants on the Continent always talk about liberty, equality and fraternity, interpreting this to mean that they can take liberties with the women of the Islands. The equality means they're equal to any other bastard in sneaking a fishing smack across the Strait of a night. When it comes to fraternisation, they're pretty good, as they learnt this off Hitler's mob during the last show.

You can't tell from Horseface's speech where he comes from, because you can see he's been long enough in this country to talk like a civilised white man; but we still want to find out where his basic allegiance lies.

The Irishman starts talking about all sorts of places over there, but he can get no response from this bloke at all, and I chuck a bit into the ring and say what a lousy mob those Welshmen are. They tried to undermine young Charlie when he came down there to be made a Prince. They were going to blow up a tunnel with him and a train in it.

This crowd are bloody handy with gelignite as well, from being used to blowing holes in the coal faces in the mines. Every mother's son of them has got a powder monkey's certificate glued onto his birth certificate. The whole trouble is only jealousy over the British throne. They're all too lousy to dob in and get a throne of their own which they could easy do. They could put one of the union bosses on it as King — which these blokes are in any case around the coalfields.

The Irishman says it'd be a bit of a ragtime kingdom just

the same, as they all look blacker than an old-time north Queensland canecutter before they got the mechanical harvesters in to do the work.

Then I tell them about the Melbourne tourist woman who says we surely can't have any racial problems up here as we've been living in an integrated society for years — ever since the white women first started to intermarry with the canecutters. She only saw them in the fields, so you can't blame her for thinking they were a race apart. Actually you can't tell a canecutter from anyone else once he's had a wash, unless you look closely and see the "Hairy Mary" in the back of his neck.

"Hairy Mary" is the fine hair growing on the leaf base of the sugar plant. It can enter the skin of a person handling it and gets bloody irritating. It's hard to rub the stuff off.

Irish says it's a different proposition with the Welshmen because if they're not down at the face digging coal, they're at home among the mullock heaps which are just as black and a bit dustier if anything, so it's hard for a Welshman to get cleaned up at any time. If they did have a proper home-grown parliament there, someone would have to invent a white biro to write with because all the bloody paper would be black.

Old Horseface doesn't bite on any of this so we reckon he can't be a Welshman, and Irish switches the line of investigation to north of the Tweed. He reckons by a process of elimination we'll get at this bloke's bloodline, and see where he fits into the stud book. So he tells the bloke about a whistle manufacturer, under contract to the railways up there to make guards' whistles. He put split peas in the whistles as an economy measure, but they had to give this away because only half the train would leave when the guard blew his whistle.

Then he tells him that the Irishmen invented the bagpipes and gave them to the Scotsmen who haven't woke up to the joke yet. He keeps telling this bloke every mean story about Scotsmen he can think of, and there's plenty, but he can't get him to bite at all.

Just then another local cattleman comes into the bar and I give him a rum without questioning his tastes, which I know. The Irishman starts in on dogs with particular reference to Scots terriers which he says are really Irish terrier, except that the ones they get in Scotland are the culls, ones that have been rejected over in Ireland through poor colour or configuration, like a Santa Gertrudis bull if he's not right up to scratch.

The cattleman tries to get in on this deal, but all he knows about is Queensland blue heelers, and for him any other sort aren't really classed as dogs. I stick my bit in now and say even the best Irish terrier are only good for turning dog chow into garden manure in this country, or barking late at night, or chewing the arse out of postmen's pants. I don't know why the Postmaster General doesn't do something about it, as it must be costing him a packet all the time for new strides for the posties. He can't get the dogs outlawed and deported (which he should because they're mean little bastards whose bite is definitely ten times worse than their bark. You're liable to get your hand badly gashed just patting the mongrels, because they have steel lathe shavings instead of hair).

Horseface shows no adverse reaction to any of this stuff, so we reckon he's not a Scotsman. He's not a pommy, because we made enough disparaging remarks about them before, and now it appears that he's not one of Harry Lauder's bunch either. The Irishman would have smelt which particular bog he came from if he was a disguised Irishman, so it only leaves the Isle of Man — but somehow this doesn't ring true to me.

They call them Manxmen over there. They had to put an "X" in, because how could you refer to yourself as a Man man? Everyone would think you were bunging on a bit of side like those poofters in the advertisements for men's cosmetics.

These Manxmen are a bit of a queer bunch too, because every year at a certain time they get up and read out all the laws of the country — if you can call it a country, because it wouldn't even rate an economic living area as a Gulf country cattle station. When they read out all the laws you're supposed to listen to them and remember the lot, even if you do have to learn parrot fashion.

One of the laws they have there says that "a Manxman may shoot a Scotsman on sight like a mad dog". I wonder what the mean bastards did to 'em? But they don't have any law like that about De Valera's crowd.

Old Horseface is showing a bit of interest in all this,and

asks what they do for a living when they're not sitting around waiting to get a Scotsman in the Winchester sights. The Irishman says they run motorbike races, and then it's not safe to be on the roads, just like in Queensland when there are no bike races on.

Anyhow, then old Horseface says, "Fill 'em all up on me," which is the only sensible remark I've heard the goon say since he first made the place look untidy. I get the stubbies and take a fair thing out of his change, then he goes out to the place where all drinkers eventually must.

"Well, he's got me," I say to the Irishman when he's gone. "Maybe he just might come from some of those wind-driven joints away off the Scottish coast like the Hebrides or the Faeroes." Actually I think the Faeroes belong to the Danes, though what anyone would want to own the place for is beyond me, except to exile political prisoners on.

If old Horseface has any family connections up north maybe he'll come in if we rubbish the place a bit. When he comes back into the bar I'm talking to the Irishman about the Hebrides, and say that the only reason anyone would stay up there would be because he couldn't scrape up the boat fare to get out. The basic wage is about as low as sharkshit, so it would be hard to put any to one side. Then the Irishman says they're a bunch of morons. All they do is fish and increase the size of their families all summer, and in winter they don't fish. All this makes no impression on the queer fellow.

Well, that's about all the Ununited Kingdom. Of course he could've come from Broken Hill, but they've got no historical background down there, being a new race that has only developed in comparatively recent years. If he does come from there, a man ought to report him to the Barrier Union because he's been in the bar half a shift and hasn't complained about the price of grog which is steep enough, Christ only knows.

Just then another car pulls up, bringing a bit more new blood into the joint. About six customers get out. You can tell they're customers because they head straight for the bar and don't muck around with bloody cameras and things. They all line up for their fodder and have no trouble making up their minds what they want, which is the sort of crowd I like, and I soon have a line-up of bottled goodness on the counter.

There are three young fellows and one old fellow and two birds. Tourists I reckon. None of 'em look like they should go through the bag wash, so I think they must've come from decent families. It looks to me as though it's going to be one of these three-cornered contests like they have in the elections, because there are only two birds and three jokers. At the same time you can't discount the old bloke either, as you can never trust the old buggers.

Well, they settle in real fast like a migrant who's determined to make good in a new country. I give them the visitors' book, and the two birds burrow into this like it's a map showing where to find a Portugoose treasure ship on one of the inner reefs of the Barrier. I say Portugoose, that being the singular of Portuguese, because there's only one ship. We've already found about all of the Spanish galleons around this part of the coast, and bloody few pieces of eight, or nine either for that matter, did we get out of 'em.

The Irishman hasn't said anything yet, but give him time. I can see his tongue flicking in and out like a Jew lizard picking up beef ants, and it won't be long before the verbal attack comes.

The old bloke starts to ask me the normal amount of useless questions, but I'm in just that nice floating condition where I don't mind a bit. He asks me all about the tin fields and says he used to do a bit of it years ago around Stanthorpe. But that was only a sort of kindergarten place the miners used to practise on before they came north to get stuck into the big 80 and 100 foot faces around Rossville, and Lode Hill at China Camp.

The young fellows have the presence of mind to wedge themselves in between the Irishman and the birds, but it doesn't do them any good because he deserts Horseface and goes down to talk to the old fellow, which puts him in number one barrier position with one of the girls and he makes the most of it. Him and the old bloke have got a fair paddock sluiced away in no time, and he picks up the bird's stubby, but not by accident — only because there's more in it than his. She sees the manoeuvre and snatches it off him.

"Sorry," he says, but he's only sorry she caught him at it.

After a while there is that much tin piling up down that

end of the bar that the counter starts to take a heavy port list, and I reckon I'll have to get the Council end loader in the morning to clean the bar out. I give one of the blokes the big slug of tin to play with because I can see he wants to play with something besides a stubby. He says how heavy it is, which is a stupid bloody remark. If it wasn't heavy, it wouldn't be tin.

Then they talk about the native cat stuffed on the wall, and the white-tailed rat, and the possum which has got the stuffing bulging out of its guts because it wasn't cured properly and which the vermin have been getting into and eating; maybe silverfish or something. I know it's not goldfish, as it's too high up on the wall.

I leave the trick matchbox loaded on the bar, and the banned book with the snake in it, in the hope of catching somebody, which is only a matter of time. I sneak in another creepy thing, which is a spider big enough to catch a dog, which springs out of its box as soon as you open the lid — if you're mug enough.

The Irishman is sluicing tin like crazy with the old fellow, taking time off to rub his rump up against one of the birds. She must be broke in, because she doesn't react violently and the same rump is bulging enticingly off the bar stool; so you can't blame him as it's a nicely rounded bit of rump.

There's so much tin piling up in the bar that I have to switch the conversation a bit. So I start talking about gold for a change, which gets 'em all in. I tell the mob all about the fabulous returns the old gold fossickers used to get and how they used to work it out "ounces to the small dish". I know they were just as big bloody liars as the average tin scratcher is today, so I divide their reputed returns by about 10,000 and arrive somewhere near an acceptable figure.

The crowd is listening to my spiel and pretty wrapped up in it, but they're all drinking on regardless because I keep ripping the heads off stubbies whenever I see an empty staring me in the face, and raking the change off the bloke who seems to have most in evidence.

I tell them about the hordes of Chinamen that busted into the gold racket. They sent so much gold home that one shipment in the *Quetta* put her down so far beyond her marks that she hit a bloody brick in Adolphus Channel (which otherwise she'd have slid over safely), that tore the bottom out of her. She went down with all hands and the cook, and the gold is still there because the tides are too strong for divers to work.

They managed to get a few tons of bullion out in other shipments, and must've had the Customs bloke on side because they only declared about as much as would be necessary to found a new dynasty over there.

They got up to all sorts of lurks to smuggle the gold out. They used to hollow out the shin bones of their mates that escaped being barbecued by the murris, and just died a natural death — like getting a knife in the back in the local fan-tan game. They used to put the gold in the shin bones, and thigh bones, and cranial cavity until the poor bastard looked like a mummified Joss. Then they'd put the bundle of bones, and and a few bullock bones as well for packing, into big stone jars, and ship the things home to China on the pretext of wanting the poor old Pong buried amongst his ancestors.

This worked all right for a while until one day the shore gang used a sling instead of a cargo net. Half a dozen of these jars spewed out of the sling and crashed into the hold, nearly killing a couple of holders that were having forty winks on a heap of dunnage. The jars burst and crunched up the bones, and all the yellow metal was strewn around the hold, and some in amongst the cargo.

Then the lumpers sung out to the bosun to chuck down a couple of brooms so they could leave the place nice and tidy, which is not like them generally. They swept up all the rubbish and put it in kerosene tins. They had to work like beavers to shift the cargo so they could get at the rest of the debris. When the whistle blew, they took everything home and banjoed it for the gold. A couple of them retired from the Watersiders Union on the strength of it and started up a new pub.

This put the Chinamen back where they started as far as the smuggling racket was concerned because they knew the lumpers would be sure to have a series of accidents after that. They had to think up a new lurk. But there's nothing to equal the cunning of a Chinamen and they soon got other dodges going to get the gold out.

If you listen to the old-timers around Cooktown about

how many Chinamen there were on the Palmer, it's a wonder China didn't complain to the United Nations (only it wasn't invented then) about the population drift. There was a fair stack of them, and at one stage they nearly outnumbered the blacks in the area.

However, the murris soon adjusted the balance of nature by putting on Chinese meals at least once a week. The main course was long pig, but there were all sorts of side dishes like Pekin duck, sweet and sour Cantonese and barbecued Hainan dog. Hungry-looking buggers, who'd been working overtime of a night digging out the wash from the white man's claims and were a bit lean, they made into chow mein.

The murris used to go for the Chinese more than the white men because they were easier to catch. The white men were a tougher proposition, as they always seemed to have a Winchester handy or a Colt Peacemaker hung on their person and the blacks always seemed to lose two or three of their party before they got the white man. After a while they woke up to the fact that if this went on too far, losing about three cannibals to one white man, they would eat themselves out of business. So after that they concentrated more on the Sons of Heaven.

Don't think I've been neglecting my customers all this time, because I haven't. The dishing out of stubbies is an automatic reflex with me, and although I might get a bit carried away and fail to take the money, I'll pick it up on the next round anyway.

During a lull in the story one of the girls lifts the matchbox and it goes off with a shuddering rattle. She lets out a squeal, nearly falling off the bar stool, and bumps the banned book trick which goes off too, scaring the hell out of the lot of them. Just when they're half crying and half laughing and sort of recovering from it all, the Irishman leans over and opens the one with the bloody spider in it for good measure. It jumps in between the two girls, and one of them gets a shock which would register about nine on the Richter scale — whatever the hell that is.

She keeps bubbling away there for quite a while, with everyone else laughing fit to kill themselves. I was hoping there was a vulcanologist handy to stick a thermometer down into her crater to see if a major eruption was imminent; or maybe a doctor that could stand in for the vulcanologist, because she was nearly ready to bust. A man'd have a job explaining away a disintegrated customer to the coppers.

But I think to myself when I look at this bunch of semi-liquid, semi-lunatic imbeciles that a psychiatrist would be more useful, and a man should keep a brace of straightjackets handy just in case.

Finally they all settle down again and I tell them a bit more about the Palmer days. Particularly about two high-class dames; one by the name of Palmer Kate, and the other called the Grecian Bend. She was known by this name because of the silhouette of her figure which was of the type very much in the fashion those days.

They were members of the oldest and most necessary profession, but still very high-class dames indeed. They must've been high-class dames, because all their clientele paid in gold. The honorarium was one ounce of fine gold, which at the ruling mint price was worth about three pounds, a considerable sum of money in that particular era.

The Irishman chips in and says it'd be just his bloody luck to have been a tin scratcher even then, as the price of tin was only about thirty shillings per hundredweight bag. If he was going to compete with the gold fossickers, he'd have had to stagger into town with *two bags* of tin, and arrive at the house of assignation exhausted.

I tell them that Palmer Kate accumulated so much gold that she didn't want to cash it at the bank. The income tax bloodhounds were always smelling around even then. So she got a lot of it smelted down and had the local jeweller, who was also a goldsmith, to fabricate a beautiful golden chamber pot out of it.

It was a work of art with scroll work all over it and "Palmer Kate" in Old English lettering embossed in bold relief on the side, because she didn't have a registered brand or earmark.

When she finally passed on in Cooktown, to the place where all good old battlers go, they couldn't find a trace of this masterpiece of the goldsmith's art.

She used to take it with her sometimes when she had to

go out bush to hunt up a bit of trade between China boats. A special packsaddle was made to carry the pot, and a well-trained packhorse put under the saddle for safety. She was pretty crook and failing when she came into Cooktown for the last time. I reckon the murri horsetailer might've saddled up the wrong horse without her noticing it. The story goes that it got stung on the backside by a swarm of yellow wasps and bolted into the bush. The murris wouldn't go after it unless she belted them over the skulls with a set of hobble chains, and she was too crook at the time to care.

That's why I reckon this fantastic treasure is still lying out along the route between the West Normanby and Hell's Gate. It'd be worth a king's ransom if a man could only retrace the route of the convoy and find it. I reckon this shouldn't be very hard if a man had the time and a few bucks for expenses, and a bit of determination.

The bar seems to go all quiet of a sudden, and you can bloody near hear all the wheels turning in their skulls. You can't tell whether the different ones are worshipping at the shrine of Eros or Mammon, so I stir 'em up a bit more.

"Just imagine what it'd bring at auction at Christie's in London. It would be a far more valuable piece than anything they got out of the sacking of Lima or Mexico City. About the only thing Henry Morgan brought back from there that was worthwhile was a few tanker trailers full of Jamaican rum. They're still bottling this stuff off to this day, and it's good stuff too. I'd drink it all the time, only I was weaned on bundy."

I can see the old Rake with a real glassy look in his eye which could have been avaricious or lascivious, I don't know which. I can see he is thinking about proposing the formation of a syndicate to go in search of the treasure. I am hoping to Christ he won't because if he does, I'd have to be in it, because the bloody yarn might be true after all. And if I went, the Irishmam would have to go too.

In any case we'd have to have him along with us to carry the monstrous thing home out of the Tiger country where it'd be sure to be, because of the weight of it. It was well known that Palmer Kate had two big strong murris in her retinue, especially detailed to decant it every morning. She made the mistake of stooping to this menial task once herself in a rush of business and finished up pulling a couple of muscles in her arm. The right arm at that — the one she always held out for the gold dust. (Through long practice she could tell within a couple of grains whether she was getting touched or not.)

I realise at this point I am doing myself out of custom, because they're not drinking real steady, being too deep in thought. That's the worst of this yarn-spilling. The bigger the bloody lie you tell them, the more likely you're believed. So I bring 'em all back to reality by saying, "Righto. Whose bung is it?" and we all jump straight back from the nineteenth century into the space age.

One young fellow is not quite satisfied about the yarn, although it was a good one, and he wants to know whether Palmer Kate numbered the Chairmen amongst her camp followers.

"Of course she did, and they were good payers too. You don't think a Chinaman would be silly enough to go hanging round a murris' camp in those days do you?"

After this old Horseface goes out the back and, wanting a bit of fresh air myself, I shortcut through the building and arrive nearly the same time as he does. I see him look at the Gentlemen sign outside, but he just ignores that and goes straight in. I think he has a bit of a queer look in his eyes, and sure enough when he comes out again he grabs a waddy and smashes a few glass louvres in one of the rooms as he goes by. Now I know just what form of lunacy he follows. It's called TIV up here — Turps Induced Vandalism. I don't go and challenge the bastard because he might have homicidal tendencies as well.

I slip back into the bar and call the Irishman to one side and tell him about this merchant, so we can both keep an eye on him. The Irishman says we'll have a rum next time, and I get the message.

So when the bloke comes back in, the Irishman orders a rum for them both. I give the Irishman an ordinary rum, and the other bloke a double OP. It's no time before he's making love to Mother Earth. We get a couple of the other blokes to give us a hand and we march him off and into his bunk. I hope to Christ he doesn't wake up till tomorrow (no such luck but at least he's out for a while), then we go back into the bar.

Just then I see a pollution trail coming down the hill. This time it doesn't resemble the ordinary commercial jet, but is more like a Sabre or F111 trail, and I'm just waiting to see what sort of a scatterbrained idiot gets out of it. Damn me, when it pulls up there's two of 'em get out, and it's just what we expected — real urgers. I get the mob to spread out a bit and we occupy all the front bar with a bit of slouching, so they have to go round into the speakeasy, which handicaps them a bit.

They get their stubbies and try to break into the party, but even the birds are not impressed, although they're young enough to get an entree with them. They are sort of ignored which upsets their ego a bit, but nobody cares what they do with their ego.

Anyway, they rip a stubby down each and want another couple which I produce promptly. The mob is talking about some dreadful road fatality which happened the day before. I say the formula to work out whether a road smash is going to happen is easy if you feed the right data into the computer — and one bloke asks what the right data is.

I say it's a sort of equation which reads HP × V × IV over ×. He says he can work out HP which is horse power, the V which is velocity. He's a bit clued up, and rightly figures that × is the number of stubbies consumed. He wants to know what IV is. I tell him this stands for inches of vacuum in the skull, this being the greatest contributing factor in road smashes. I see the two urgers trying to figure this lot out, but they can't because of their IV being too high.

The Irishman starts to make cracks in their direction. Sometimes I think I should go in to the local magistrate and get a restraining order out against the animal. He keeps at it, and I can see these blokes trying not to lose their cool but they've got the job ahead of them with the Irishman.

"How long have you blokes been non-members of the 206 Club?" he says finally. "Or are you still in it?"

"What's the 206 Club?"

"Two hundred dollars and six months," says Irish, and by the look they give him and the look they exchange, he may just have hit the nail on the head.

I bet if the Sergeant bulged his way into the bar at the moment, these blokes would really pack it, and a man might make a cheap purchase of a souped-up UF Model (that means undertaker's friend), right on the spot.

Well, these characters can't stand the competition. They buy a six-pack for the road, and retire from the battle scene. But they have the last say because, as they wheel the bomb round and pour on the jet fuel, they spin the wheels and throw so much gravel and stones into the bar that I think it must be a student riot — which in a way it is.

Well, the other crowd finally decide they have had enough, and they say they're going to push on to Cooktown for a look around. After they swamp the last of their stubbies and get a couple of six-packs for the road (which they don't need but only buy to be sociable), they pull out of the bar, all saying "Goodbye" and "See you sometime". The old bloke says, "We'll be back!" (and I know what's in this old bastard's mind).

"Sooner than you think," calls out one of the girls.

They pile in and take off nice and easy, like good respectable drunks should. Not like those other types who want to arrive dead on time.

A man has time to relax for a while, as sometimes it's a relief to get rid of all customers. If you had 'em all the time, you'd finish up as mad as they are.

As the Bloomfield mailman said to me one day when we noticed a joker behaving a bit queerly, "It's funny how a bloke doesn't notice it when he loses a few of his marbles . . . but everyone else does."

"You can't blame that poor bugger," I said. "He can't help it. It's just that he's unlucky in being part of a minority. If his type were in the majority, we'd be inside looking out instead of the other way round . . ."

The Irishman has pranged onto the couch again, and I don't wonder at it. He must get terrible tired — carrying all that grog around. Just then another couple of murri fellows come along in an old jalopy and pull up.

The driver is obviously a ringer from a station and the purse man as well. I know the bloke with him — the only work he's ever performed are the normal functions of nature.

The driver however is pretty lively and really dolled up, wearing a cream-coloured ten-gallon hat, shiny, new, bright-yellow ringer boots, green strides and of course the usual red shirt with a white bull's head embroidered into the pocket. He looks just like Butch Cassidy in technicolour.

They come into the bar and say, "Good day boss."

"Good day," I say. "Where you feller come from?"

"King Junction," says this bloke, and I wonder how he could arrive here so sober after passing through two pubs on the way.

"You never stop in Laura eh? Why"?

"We been playin' up a bit there last time," he says, "and that publican he say, 'You gettabluttyhelloutahere.' So we come to dis place."

"Well, don't bloody well play up here either," I say.

"We won't boss. We can get coupla stumpies, eh?" So I dish out the stubbies and they relax on the high stools.

"Where you goin'?"

"Bloomfield," he says, but the nearest any murri can get to it is "Bloombill".

After a few more beers they decide to push on and the purse man buys a "gallon o' jar" — which is a gallon jar of wine, and is called a gallon o' jar to distinguish it from a gallon plastic container which is the one they don't like.

Just before they go, the other bloke puts the hard word on me for credit, which I am reluctant to give as he has no job and no dough. I know it'll be hard to extract it out of him later, so I knock him back. But he renews his plea and says, "I pay you next week."

"How you going to pay me next week? You not working."

"I get it from my missus next week," he says. "She get that . . . you know . . . what you call 'im — child enjoyment cheque."

I've got a bit of a soft spot for the buggers, but after doing a stretch of ten years in a bush pub (no time off for good behaviour either), like a beast in bad buffalo-fly country, I've built up an immunity to nearly every form of bite.

"Why don't you wait till next week after your missus gets the cheque?" I say. "Then you can come back here and drink on. That way you'll be thirstier still, and you'll enjoy it more." But he doesn't subscribe to this sort of reasoning.

Away they go, and a big truck pulls in. The truckie comes

in and says Fourex, and I get it for him. "Can you loan me a big hammer," he says. "I've got some tyre trouble."

So I go out and get him a seven pound sledge hammer and say, "This do?"

"Good," he says, and after a couple more he goes out and repairs a couple of tyres after pulling nails out of them.

When he's finished, he leaves the hammer against a post on the verandah, and has a couple more before he takes off. The sound of his diesel starting up wakes the Irishman, but the truckie escapes just in time. He just doesn't know how lucky he was. He might never have got away if the Irishman pinned him down because it's like trying to beat a mongoose off a cobra once he gets on your back. He seems terrible crooked about missing this bloke whom he knows, and feels slighted because the bloke didn't stop.

Just then Horseface comes up for air, looking like something that's been through the polar bear's cage at Taronga Park. He says, "Give us a stubby, mate," and I say a man ought to cut his bloody grog off after that last performance. He says he'll pay for the damage.

"I know bloody well you will," I say.

Then I go out and count how many louvres are broken, adding in a couple that've been broken before in a genuine drunk's accident. There's ten all told. I say they cost a dollar each to buy, and with transport and cost of fitting, two dollars each; I want twenty dollars. So he peels this off without argument, and I say don't do it again. He's sucking his stubby and looking like a mongrel dog that's just been given a whipping. I feel half sorry for him. Then the Irishman joins him and it's on again.

The phone rings, and a bloke from Lakeland Downs, who I know, says, "I thought I should be fair and warn you; there's about twenty of us coming in tonight. See that you have plenty of dough there to cash about twenty cheques." So I say OK, see you later, and it looks as though it's going to be a hard day's night for me.

I come back into the bar and remind old Horseface that if there's any more destruction of property, he can start walking. He is very contrite and says, "No problems," and I believe him . . . unfortunately.

Well, the day's wearing on, and I manage to get the two of

them, plus the cattleman, who's still here, to have a feed and I get the nosebag on myself. Even a bloody pop singer must eat.

Well, the Irishman teams up with the cattleman and Horseface, and they look like getting a head start on the crowd that's coming tonight just in case the grog runs short. There's no danger of this because a publican without beer is just as good as a bridegroom in a plaster cast, and I'd hate to get in that position . . . I mean, without beer.

It's not long after that when the first of the funsters arrive and start piling out of their cars. There's a solid pollution trail coming down the hill, but we can't see much of it as it's nearly dark now and it's going to be darker still before the night's out, in more ways than one.

Well, they finally get the whole party there and there's well over thirty all told because they didn't count the wives, popsies, and assorted kids they've brought along.

We get all these into the lounge so they won't interfere with the drinking too much, although some of them can mark time with the men in this regard. Then I start beheading stubbies as fast as I can and lining them up on the bar. I can see some of this lot wanting to hook into it straight away, but they're still gentlemen at this stage, and wait till they all get lined up. I start one end and pick up the dough from the first bloke, he says, "What about your own?" which I'd forgotten in the press of business.

So I lift a stubby up and everyone says "Cheers" at once, and it's on for young and old.

Then someone has the presence of mind to say, "What about the women?" So they see what *they* want (in the way of drink, anyway). The kids get Coke and orange and all sorts of things.

Everyone is talking at once and no-one listening in particular. They pull the Irishman and the other two into the shout, so I only have to take the loot off one bloke at a time, which simplifies things a bit.

The night wears slowly on and the crowd starts to warm up a bit. They get stuck into the piano and start singing songs old and new, but the old ones get priority. The new ones are only gammon songs anyway. Then someone wants some of the Beatles', but they get howled down on this deal.

Then one character starts to really hammer into the old piano, just like old Paderewski with St Vitus dance. We don't know how old the piano is, or who made it even, as the maker's name has been scratched off the lid by drunks' fingernails missing the keyboard, but she still plays all right. It has a cunning gadget on it down the bottom end of the keyboard which is a volume control. I've already got this pulled back nearly to zero which the bloke playing doesn't know about. He feels he's not making enough noise, so he opens up the top of the noise box and some mug spills a glass of beer down into the guts of the machine and deadens about a full octave of keys.

This doesn't worry the pianist any as he just moves the stool along a bit and keeps on playing a full octave lower. A couple of the singers nearly strain their larynxes trying to adjust to the new key.

Then they start buying special beers for this piano merchant and he has to put the lid down again to stack the beers that are piling up on him. He is too busy playing, in fact, to have time to drink them all. He gets so worked up, I think any time now he's going to tip the lot over as his savage attack on the old piano is shaking hell out of things. I can see a fine flow of dust coming out the bottom where he's crunched up a hornet's nest amongst the keys.

Well, they are all talking and singing and some laughing and some half crying at jokes, and blokes are hanging tales on each other, and the trick snake is soiling a few change-dailies and the bloody jack-in-the-box spider nearly causes a few heart failures. Things are really swinging.

I can see Horseface walking around with a wild glazed look in his eye, and I am thankful I went and hid the woodheap axe a while before. I have a feeling this goon is going to perform again before the night's out.

Just then the first two murris arrive back from Cooktown — they didn't stay after all — and want to be in it too, and we don't mind adding a bit of new blood to the party.

One bloke says, "Boss, you been pickin' up some money when we feller leave here?" and I now know which bloke it belongs to. So I go and get the envelope off the shelf with the address written in a language they can understand, and give it to him.

"Well, seeing as you might have lost it anyway, what about you feller shout eh?"

"OK, I shout. Pill 'em all up."

The kids are playing ring-a-rosie or something on the verandah, and there are a few dog scuffles on the side where my blue heeler and the bull terrier are defending their own dunghill against all comers, of which there are quite a few amongst the visitors' dogs.

There are dogs of all pedigrees, and a bloody lot without — ranging from cornbeef setters to potlickers and tripe hounds, right up to Rhodesian Ridgebacks.

Next thing there's a dogfight in the bar and a bloke is trying to pull my blue heeler off his animal, but the Irishman intervenes and says it's a fair fight and to let 'em go, so then there's a good sort of a manfight on and the dogfight is forgotten. Strangely enough the dogs stop fighting now as this is far more fun to watch and they don't get bitten or kicked either — and the fight gets a bit willing for a while.

They have flying bedsteads in England, and flying saucers in all part of the world, mostly seen by blokes that are just going into the horrors or just coming out of them, but our major visitation here is flying bar stools. You have to look out for yourself. It's a sort of occupational hazard.

After a while the mob breaks the fight down and they all settle in for a bit more steady drinking which is what they came for in the first place. The fights are only incidental entertainment. They break a few stubbies on the floor, and one bar stool is declared unserviceable. There are a couple of glasses among the casualties too; I always said they should be barred. Someone gets the broom and sweeps up the wreckage and things return to normal.

Just then there's a crash of breaking glass outside and I know instantly what its origin will be. Sure enough we rush out to find Horseface up to his old tricks. The Irishman gives me a hand and we give him the bums rush into his room and slam the door on him.

"Right-o mate," I say. "No more grog. You've got the Dog Act on you as from now. Any more of it tonight and I'll call the coppers."

He doesn't fight back, being too sick or silly, or both, and we return to the festivities.

The pressure is really on and we have a change of murderer at the piano, more savage if anything, but it makes the mob happy. They're getting into "Mother Machree", and that Scottish song which starts off, "Have you ever been across the sea to Ireland?". It must be Scottish otherwise they wouldn't ask you this question.

The Irishman asks me what lunatic asylum old Horseface escaped from, but I say we'll find out next week when we read the papers. There's sure to be a description of him in there somewhere.

By now the sexes are fully integrated, and they're milling all over the place and in the bar as well. I don't see any of the *wreaker* sex trying to shout the bar, but they still don't miss out on a drink just the same. There's one slashing blonde from Lakeland who is the centre of attraction and the target of numerous amorous barbs from the men, and barbs of pure bloody jealousy from the women.

They call her the Wrench out there, because she's always upsetting the machinery of the place. The Irishman has the inside running for a while, but he can't stand the competition as the grog is his main weakness, the birds being in his opinion only a necessary evil.

The music goes on without a stop, and the singing — though sometimes a bit off key — is getting easier to listen to under the soothing effect of the popular drug of one's choice. Some of the songsters are not only singing in a different key, but also a different song, but who cares.

The trick matchbox catches some poor bastard every time I remember to wind it up. One girl sees the big python skins hanging up on the bar wall and exclaims, "*Ooh*. Look at the crocodile skins."

"They're not crocodile skin," says a know-all bloke. "They're snake skins."

"No," says Irish, "they're crocodile skins."

"Get out," says the bloke. "Crocodiles have legs and there're no legs on these skins."

Irish sticks to his story and says that the biggest one came off a crocodile that had been in a fight with a cleanskin bull and had his legs kicked off before we caught and skinned him. The bloke looks a bit dubious about this, but doesn't know whether to argue or not.

Then the snake yarns start in earnest. I tell them about a bloke walking along the road at night in front of the Cooktown hospital. "A brown snake bit him, and he said, 'You bastard. You'll die before I do,' and he grabbed what he thought was a stick to kill him with. It turned out to be another brown snake, and it bit him too."

"Did he live?" says one bloke.

"Yes," I said, "he got over it all right, being a good old rum drinker . . . but they had to send the two snakes away to the pathologist to see what they died of."

I think the Irishman is going to bring his chainsaw into the bar in case another big python attacks him, but thank goodness this doesn't eventuate. Instead he tells the mob about a big python up at the Black Mountain that took two days to cross the road . . . you couldn't work out whether it was very, very long, or just slow. Then they start talking about snakes swallowing wallabies and all that sort of thing.

Irish says he lost a horse once and found it in a snake's guts, and the mob howls him down, but he sticks to his guns. Somebody says, "God hates liars," and the Irishman says he can prove it because he still has the horse with him. He was a white horse, and that's how he found him so easily. One bloke wanted to bet him that it just could not happen, but Irish says, "Listen mate. I just don't want to take your money on a bet like that," and he pulls out of his pocket one of those little white horses that come from around the neck of White Horse Whiskey, saying, "There's the horse to prove that I got him back."

There is a steady run of kids needing soft drinks and lollies, chocolates and peanuts etc., because by now the adults have got enough turps into them to be expansive and big-hearted. The kids are making the most of the situation.

Then they all start buying expensive types of bubbly wines and liqueurs as if they aren't getting silly enough on beer anyway, and they all talk about going home, but don't. It's long past closing time and I have to warn them that the coppers might come along any time now, but they only laugh at me. They know they only have one paddy waggon in town and couldn't fit them all in it, so there's not much I can do about it.

PADERWHISKY IN ACTION

Somebody says, "Fill 'em up again," so we start a new round of drinks. Just then one of the ringer types comes in with about seven feet of writhing black-headed python draped around him, and all the girls squeal. The poor bloody docile snake can't stand all the noise, and slides into the ringer's shirt for safety.

After he gets safely curled up in the bloke's shirt, he sticks his head out again between the buttons and has a look around. I'm sure he's wagging his head in sorrowful bewilderment at the spectacle of all these idiots performing.

My missus comes into the bar and says, "Get that damned snake out of the bar or I'll get the shotgun and shoot him."

"He won't hurt anyone, missus," says the bloke. "He's harmless."

"He will be harmless if you don't get rid of him."

So the bloke reluctantly takes the thing outside to let him go.

Well, the music starts up again and they go through some of the old tunes, every mug singing out for a request number at once. The pianist is playing any blasted thing that comes into his head, with the mob all trying to follow it, chipping in with about one bar in three but all enjoying it just the same.

Then one bloke who has been up in the Northern Territory comes in with about eight feet of two-inch polythene pipe and starts playing the didgeridoo to accompany the artist. He plays it fairly good, but he's only got about sixty-six per cent of the notes that the myall murris play in Arnhem Land . . . he's got two notes, and they've got three, but it adds to the merriment. Things are going so swimmingly at the moment with everyone singing or laughing, I feel that I should close all the doors and windows just to keep the fun in, but it'd be too damned hot.

The music stops for a moment and somebody suggest they all have turn about at contributing an act or a song, so it's on again and several have a go at recitations, and another bloke sings a bit of a ditty. One bloke wants to sing a parody on a song, but we can't let him carry on with that one and howl him down. Then the Irishman starts off with "The Rose of Tralee" and they all join in.

After this lot they want me to sing, but I say I can't sing. Then they want me to play something, but I tell them I'd play them some pornographic music . . . only I've got no pornograph.

Well, I can see that it's nearly time to get them moving on the way home, so I say, "Who wants to put their orders in now?" and a couple of blokes start in on a bit of panic-buying in case there's not enough to go round. The next thing they're all demanding cartons of stubbies, bottles of rum and whiskey and jars of wine etc., in case they get thirsty going home. For a while there I am as busy as the scroungers at Doomben picking up discarded betting slips after a race.

Eventually they have all got enough supplies for the road and start packing kids and dogs into vehicles. One bloke is growling at a kid for getting out again and forces him back in about three times. Finally the kid says, "But Daddy, that's not our Holden." So the bloke looks around and he walks over to another Holden out of which protrudes a well-padded female bottom. Slapping this, he says, "Come on, love. Hurry up, we've got to get home," and a strange female voice says, "Go and find your own wife's bum to slap."

"Christ," he says. "A man can't win." Then to the kid, "Where *is* our car?"

Then comes the usual drunk's routine, like the Sydney Symphony Orchestra warming up, of starting engines and stopping them again, and saying, "Where the hell is my wife?" — and wives wandering round like fowls with their heads off saying, "Where's that idiot husband of mine?" — and trying to put the wrong mongrel dog in the right car and the right mongrel in the wrong car, and the dogs getting out again as fast as they're put in — and the blokes singing out, "Where is that carton of stubbies I left here?" — and nobody caring much as it'll all come out in the wash.

Then other blokes want packets of cigarettes, and kids are saying, "Mummy, you promised to buy me some Twisties and potato crisps." "Bugger the crispies," says Mummy. "Where's the bottle of burgundy I bought to make the cake with?" And Daddy's saying, "I can just imagine you putting good stuff like that into a cake."

There are engines starting up all around and roaring their heads off and some blokes starting to move out and giving a few bumper bars a bit of a crunch, none of which they notice very much. Then some of them start singing out "Goodbye," and "See you again," and one girl says, "Don't use up all the fun before we come again."

One bloke jumps his car into ahead gear instead of astern, and someone yellow out, "Look out you bloody mug!"

"Who's a bloody mug?"

"Come on," says his wife. "Come on, never mind causing bloody arguments at this time of the morning."

"It's bloody night . . . not morning."

"It's near enough to morning. It will be by the time we get home at this bloody rate."

Then there are numerous car doors slamming, and engines grumbling away with no mufflers because they've been torn off on the road coming down here; kids singing out for mothers, and dogs snarling at each other; a bloke whinging because he can't find two cartons of beer he bought, and his wife saying, "Don't be so bloody stupid. They're in the boot." Then her saying, "I think I'd better drive," and him, "Who owns this bloody car anyway? — and the Irishman shaking hands all round and swearing everlasting friendship and to hell with the IRA anyhow.

Then the lead cars get straightened out and take off with blaring horns. A steady tail hooks onto them, and we can see them going up the hill as though they are all connected up to each other by two ropes. Stragglers are singing out, "Goodbye," and "See you some more," and more horns are blowing, doors slamming and drunks yakai-ing. One bloke who's seen too many Yank westerns, sings out, "Yippee," and "Ride 'em cowboy," and we can still hear the horns blowing as the last tail lights fade out of sight.

4

I turn round thankfully to get the place closed up so I can get to bed, and the bloody Sinn Fein drop-out of an Irishman says, "Thank Christ that bunch has gone. Now we can have a nice drink in peace and quite." Wouldn't it!

"Well," I say, "just one, and that's it." There's enough grog in half-emptied stubbies on the bar to keep a drunk going for a week.

"Bring out two fresh ones," he says. Then the two murris come in and want a stubby each, so I give them a couple and tell them to get to hell out of it and go and sleep it off in their car. I steer them out of the bar and close up the doors behind them.

I look at all the bloody empties, cigarette packets (some of them half full too, but I'm smoking too much as it is), chocolate wrappings, empty Twisties packets and spilt beer on the floor. I know the lounge is worse; just like the Show Grounds on the last day of the Show. I realise the job is too big for me, but I've still got to pack the fridges otherwise there'll be no cold beer for the morning. So with a bit of Irish help I hook into it and fill up all the fridges, then crawl thankfully into bed. Ah well, all in a day's work.

I'm only asleep about an hour when I hear some bloke calling out for me and I get up ready to open hostilities. There are two jokers outside, and the tell me they're in trouble down at the road junction, having run a photo finish. The two cars are so heavily telescoped into each other that they can't get them apart.

So I get wearily dressed and the Irishman gets up too, and we take my Toyota and his Land Rover and drive down to the scene of the prang.

When we get there, the cars look like two of Frankenstein's monsters in a silent struggle to the death. We know they won't bite us and move in with towing chains, which is the main part of a traveller's equipment in this country. We get the two vehicles hooked on, and after a couple of preliminary jerks, get them down to a steady scratch pull and finally heave them apart. After this we have to get a crow bar to lever the mud guards off the wheels so they can turn. Strangely enough both vehicles are returned to a state of mobility so we don't have to tow them, but both sets of headlights are pulverised. So we take off with me leading one bloke and Irish the other. We get back to the pub where I tell them to park out of the way under the mango tree, with their front ends poked up alongside the verandah.

Of course both these blokes, being commercial travellers, want a drink. This in fact appears to be the reason for the crash. One bloke was just turning in onto our road as the other bloke was hurrying on into Cooktown. One bloke says he's only had his new Valiant a week. The other says he's only had his a fortnight.

Of course the Irishman needs a drink as well by this time, and it's a while before we can get the bar cleared again. I tell these blokes which rooms to take; and to get up early to catch the mailman into town as they want to get the mechanic out onto the job. Once more I get to bed. Some time after daylight I get up and stir the stale beer in the Irishman so he can give me a hand to clean up, which we do before breakfast. Then we go and have a look at the two cars, which are really battered up in front. They are parked noses into the verandah, right in front of old Horseface's room. I see the seven pound hammer which I'd loaned the to the truckie; then I see the Irishman, the cunning bastard, rub some of the red paint off one of the smashed cars onto the face of the hammer. He puts it down on the verandah in front of old Horseface's room, and we go back to the bar.

We can hear him getting busy in his room, and we know it won't be long before he comes to life. Finally he comes out of the room yawing and stretching and making rude noises. The he gives a might gasp as he catches sight of the vehicles and his eyes stick out so far that you could sit on them to give him a haircut.

Just them the Irishman saunters slowly out, pretending he doesn't see him, and picks up the hammer, wagging his head sadly. He looks at the cars, all the time under the close scrutiny of old Horseface. Carefully he picks a bit of red paint off the hammer head and wagging his head sadly again, drops the hammer and comes back into the bar.

We can hear a low moaning whine from Horseface and the next thing he comes staggering into the bar holding his head in his two hands and screwing it from side to side as though trying to pull it off. He slumps down on a bar stool and mumbles, "For Christ sake, give me a drink," but I am in front of him as I already have a double OP rum poured out for him, knowing he is going to need it.

He gulps this down, nearly choking in the process and has tears in his eyes when he looks at me, both from the rum burning him and the alcoholic remorse. He looks gastly and he says in a strangled voice, "Have you called the cops yet?"

"No," I say, "the cops are both away out at Laura and won't be back till tomorrow." This only extracts a low moan from him.

The Irishman goes out and pick up the hammer and come back into the bar and hands it over to me with a side glance at Horseface as he does so. Horseface sees the hammer going over and gives another pitiful moan, and says, "What am I going to do? Christ there must be 1000 dollars worth of damage."

"I don't know, mister," I say. "But you better play it cool."

"Where are the owners?"

"They've gone into Cooktown to try and get the cops but the won't be able to. The best thing you can do is to get on the bus when she comes in this morning, and get to hell out of here."

It's all I can do to stop laughing, and the Irishman looks fit to burst a gut trying to hold himself in. Just then the two owners come back with the mechanic in his car and they start to do things around the cars.

Horseface looks fearfully out of the bar, and just then one bloke pick up a big tyre lever which he is going to use to pry open the bonnet, but Horseface thinks he's in for an attack. He's tempted to go out and face them and get it all over with, but we stop him as we know if that happens they'll think he's madder than he looks. Furthermore if he does go out and things get straightened out, he's likely to to take the bloody hammer to the Irishman and me when he finds out how we've been having him on.

So we tell him in hoarse, urgent voices to "not be a bloody fool". If he stays in here with us he'll be safe.

One bloke pulls out the dip stick to check the oil and the

Irishman says, "What's that he's got? A bloody stiletto or something." Horseface has one quick horrified glance, gives a low moan and huddles down into the corner of the bar.

Just then we see the bus coming down the hill, and I tell Horseface to go out the back way to his room and bring his gear in to the bar to make a quick getaway, which he does. While he is away, Irish and I relieve our built-up pressure a bit, but we can't really laugh out loud.

Well, the bus pulls in and there aren't many passengers, only a couple getting off for a quick drink. Horseface comes sneaking back in with his suitcase and hides again in the same corner. The Irishman tries to calm him, but he's nearly frantic waiting for the bus to get going. I tell him not to go out until the bus is just about to leave, otherwise the two jokers might get onto him. While he's with us he's safe.

"Listen mate," I say then. "What about squaring up for your board?"

"Christ, I'm sorry." he says, bring out the wallet and settles the bill. I don't forget to make him fork over for the second set of louvers he broke as well.

"You've been bloody decent to me," he says. "It's nice to know a man has some bloody friend left in the world."

The bus driver is hounding his charges onto the bus, and we hold Horseface to the last moment until the bus engine starts and she's almost ready to roll. Then he just about breaks a couple of my metacarpal bones, pumps the Irishman's arm that hard I think he's going to pull it out of its socket, says, "Thank Christ there are a few bloody white men left in the world." gives a whinny like an old mare defending her foal against the dingoes, a sweep out of the bar with head lowered and make a pierhead jump for the bus just as she starts to move.

Thank goodness the roar of the bus engine taking off under load drowns out the howls of the bloody mirth issuing from Irishman and myself. We fairly roll around the bar unable to stop laughing about the whole deal until my wife comes in and says, "What's wrong with you imbeciles?" But we can't tell her for laughing, with the tears running out of our eyes, she so departs with a shot at us about how we should be put under some form of restraint.

Just as we are getting over the attack the two owners

come in and want to know what it's all about. Between bursts of laughter we tell them the story, and this starts them off and they can hardly down a drink through laughing as well.

They say they've got their vehicles good enough to get back on the road. One bloke put a ten dollar bill in front of me and the other bloke hands one to the Irishman, saying that was for pulling them apart. we accept the tips, as they say they can put it on the swindle sheet.

We get back to talking about old Horseface again. Irish says it's going to be funny when they overtake the bus, as he'll be looking out for them.

"Steam slowly past the bus at Lakeland Downs when they pull up there, like a prowl car," I say, "and look staring into the bus. You won't see him as he'll probably be hiding under the seat. After they leave Lakeland, come from behind, like Georgie Moore, through the dust cloud, and park at the Palmer with the bent ends of the cars staring him in the face when the bus pulls in."

But the blokes won't be in it. They reckon they couldn't even do it to a dog. They say we might be being too rough on the poor bastard, but we say that we want to cure him of his bad habits, the louvre-smashing drongo. We bet he won't be able to look at a big hammer again without shuddering, and every time he goes past the wrecking yard he'll cringe.

Anyway, we have another good laugh about it all, and the two bagmen shout again. The two murris come into the bar and they shout for them, too. The murris haven't been game to come in before as they were convinced the Irishman and I weren't safe too approach.

After a couple more, it look as though the two bagmen are going to settle in for a steady session, but in due course the reluctantly tear themselves up by the roots and get into their battered cars, working out what sort of a good yarn they'll tell to explain how it happened. I tell them I've never seen them and the Irishman says he wouldn't know them if he picked them out of the soup. So they drive away with easy minds, and we set into a bit of steady drinking.

The two murri fellows finally decide they'd better get along as it's a long way to where they're going. I know they won't make it today as they want a bottle of rum, two bottles of wine and a carton of stubbies. The weight if all this bottled lunancy is going to beat them, and if they don't meet one of their mates along the road as an excuse to get stuck into it they will by themselves anyway, for fear the stuff might go bad.

While I am getting their supplies for the road, I see the Irishman attaching a four gallon drum with a length of wire to the back bumper bar of their vehicle. I think they may not hear the clatter it's going to make above all the other grinding noises that issue from under the bonnet as a normal accompaniment to travel in the bomb they've got.

He carefully hides the drum under the back of the car so they won't stumble over it as they're getting in. He comes back and forces another drink on them. I hope he doesn't get too lavish, otherwise we won't see them go at all. I've got a bit of a soft spot for these poor buggers, and don't won't them to get into too much strife. Besides, there are two more pubs to go through before they get home.

Finally they take off with a clashing of gears and much waving of arms and wild steering. The driver is so long in second gear, I wonder if anyone's ever told him about the other one.

Eventually they get her to escape orbit and are just going up the hill, when the sound of the empty drum bashing around behind sinks into their craniums. They make a sudden stop. They both get out to investigate, obviously leaving her out of gear, because she takes off stern first with the two of them wrenching at the door handles, trying to get in to stop her. She finishes up at the bottom of the slope, being only saved from going into the creek by a fence post which someone has providentially placed there.

The black fellow's built-in sense of humour comes to their aid, and we can see them doubled up with laughter. Finally they discover the drum and another spasm of mirth follows. After disconnecting the drum, they clamber in and take off again in a cloud of dust.

We have hardly seen the tail of the before another pollution trail comes spearing down the hill. When the car arrives, we see that it's the crowd we had yesterday, the ones we told the yarn to about Palmer Kate and her contemporary. They all pile out of the vehicle and the girls are singing out, "We told you we'd be back." Irish is welcoming them back as if he own the bloody pub instead of me, and they're all shaking hands as though they've been away for fifteen years, instead of less than a day. Then they all pile into the bar and take up their barrier positions as though they also had a propriety interest in the joint.

Someone says, "Righto, line 'em up," and there's no need to ask what they want as I remember them from yesterday. They tell us about the trip into Cooktown, about Captain Cook's monument, and about the big well near it, which is the biggest well they've ever seen.

One girl says that the water didn't look to good as there were a lot of dead toads floating in it. I tell her not to worry about that as none of that Cooktown bunch would be guilty of drinking water in any case.

Not much fun in the big smoke today, I reckon. Everywhere you go to park there're voiceless, threatening, armless bandits demanding money. If you don't pay up the bloodhounds come round and stick threatening letter under your windscreen wiper, and you haven't done a bloody thing — only switched your engine off for a few minutes to cool it down. If I put a line of these half-clock faced, inarticulate, unarmed banditti up in front of my pub, I might as well close down. Everyone'd go into Cooktown to drink.

The mob down there seem able to cop it though. makes a man wonder whether they *like* to be hounded around and pushed into line. Ah well! It's nice to go down to the city now and then, but it's nicer to get away from the place, even though the road home is the longest unregistered wrecking yard in the country. When you get back home, the coppers are too busy making one-fingered typewritten reports to worry about whether you have a tail light on your truck or not. As Lennie, an old tin scratcher who's has wandered in, points out, the only reason you want a tail light is when the mug behind you has no headlight. To make matter worse, all of the coppers down round the city are totally devoid of any sense of humour; suppose you can't blame 'em when you think of the type of bloody nong-nong they have to put through the dip all the time. Give me the bush, any old day of the week. Whose shout is it?

Somebody comes up with the bright suggestion that it ought to be my shout seeing I'm so pleased to be among civilised people. The Irishman says I wouldn't shout if a crocodile bit me, and just to prove the bog trotter was wrong, I say, "Righto, it's my bung." In a matter of seconds the bar is packed. Where they come from I don't know; must of come out of hollow logs.

Anyway, this gets business off again to a flying start, because even the blokes that zeroed in on the publican's shout have to front up again eventually. Then a bloke wants a fill-up at the petrol bowser and when he comes to pay for it, he's flabbergasted. "Christ," he says, "that's a bit steep isn't it?"

"Well, that's the price the oil companies charge me, plus a bit," I say, and I admit the price has gone real high today, so high in fact that the school kids can't even afford to sniff it any more.

Another bloke chips in and says "Everything has gone up today. The only two things still coming down is rain and panties, and this year even the rain is in short supply."

Just then a batch of the Bloomfield boys arrive in a battered old jalopy, and having survived a rather long drought down there, they proceed to make up for lost time. Having filled themselves up comfortably for the time being, they proceed to lay in good stocks to take along with them, and upon departure are carrying quite a number of gallon jars to tide them over the trip ahead. Late that night we hear that they only got as far as Rossville six mile away before they started in on their take-home supplies. Later on they came back to the pub to fill up again — not petrol, but more grog supplies. Knowing the number of gallon jars they took and the number of miles they'd travelled, a quick calculation shows they'd only done about half a mile to the gallon, which is rather good consumption in a way.

It transpires that one of the community, a rather elderly chap, has passed away and the grog supplies are to hold a bit of a wake after the funeral, which is to be the next day. Someone says to old Lennie, "Are you going to old Sour Dough's funeral? You were pretty good mates with him weren't you?"

"No way," says old Lennie. "Why should I go to his funeral? After all there's no way he'll be at mine."

Attention is now diverted to the arrival of another visitor

in a battered old Land Rover which arrive in front of the pub. Out crawls a bearded young fellow from the tin fields — another tin scratcher, named Vic, who is a regular visitor to the Den, coming down for stores and of course the usual binge. Numerous greeting to the newcomer are called out as he approaches the bar.

"How are yer, Vic? C'mon, have a drink!" and others are saying, "How's the tin mine going?" and "When are yer going to sell yer mine, Vic?" He ignors it all until he has a stubby in his hand and takes a good steady slurp at it. Then he says, "G'day, g'day, g'day. How are you all?"

Later a bloke says to him, "What did yer do with the other mine yer had, Vic?"

He says, "Oh, I sold that one. Made a big quid out of it, too."

Then the bloke says, "If you made a big quid out of it, what'd yer do with the money?"

"Oh, I just done it."

"How did you get rid of such a lot of dough?"

"Well," he says, "I had a couple of heavy plunges on the horses . . . then I gave the grog a good bash as well over a long period . . . and of course the women got away with a fair swag of it too."

"What did you do with the rest of it, Vic?"

"Well," he says, "the rest of it . . . well . . . I guess . . . er . . . I must have just spent that foolishly."

Another bloke chips in and says, "What sort of a mine you got this time?"

"Orright, but she's nearly worked out now. I'll be pleased anyway, because she's a real stony bastard. Stones! Struth, you've never seen so many bloody stones and rocks of all bloody sizes and shapes. A real good place to hold one of those Irish rock festivals — you know, where they stone the orchestra to death if they don't like the bloody music. Only bloody rocks I want to see from now on is in a glass with whiskey poured over 'em!"

The talk in the bar turns to fishing, but as soon as the fish yarns start, I introduce my favourite "whopper stopper" which is a strong piece of string, about three feet long with a little loop at each end. As soon as a bloke starts telling about the big one he caught (or that got away), I slip the two loops over his thumbs and thus keep the catch in realistic limits.

They start talking about big barra, mostly in the lagoons in the Peninsula. One bloke says a lagoon dried up on Lakefield Station and the only thing in it was one really big barra, dead of course. He was so big he had *two* pelicans standing on him while they ate him.

Then I tell them about a bloke down at the Bloomfield who had staked a barra net in the river. He is quietly hauling himself and the boat along the net in the morning, unmeshing the fish he's caught overnight, when another chap rows out of a mangrove creek nearby and ranges up alongside him and says, "Good day."

The bloke answers him in like strain and carries on with emptying the net.

Finally the newcomer says quietly to him, "Do you know who I am, mister?"

"Wouldn't have a clue," says the bloke.

"Do you know you are illegally netting fish?"

"So what," says the bloke.

The newcomer says, "Well, I'm the Fisheries Inspector , that's what."

"Gee," the bloke says, "for a start I was real worried. I though you might be the bloke that owns this net."

Then I tell the about the bloke who goes fishing off the Cooktown wharf. I had given him some mud herring for bait as this is about the best bait for the fish around the wharf. When he came back later with nothing I said, "What, no fish? What happened?"

"Bait's no good," he said.

"What's wrong with the bait?"

"Too weak."

"What do you mean, too weak?"

He says he caught a doggie mackerel with the herring, then a dirty big Spanish mackerel grabs him, then bobs a bloody great barracouta which grabs the Spaniard. "I nearly had 'em all landed on the wharf when the mud herring let go and I lost the flamin' lot. I told you, didn't I. Baits no good. Too weak in the jaws."

The Irishman says he knows the bloke I'm talking about

and it was just what you'd expect from him. I query the Irishman on this, as I think he has got his characters mixed up.

"O' course I know him," he says. "I'd recognise his hide anywhere. Even plaited into a whip."

"That's a rather drastic measure to take — just so you can recognise a bloke."

"Ahrr," he says, "you take it up the wrong way."

"Don't make any wide accusations against me or I'll flatten you with the bung starter, you scourge of Erin."

So he goes into the turtle act, and peace reigns for the time being.

I tell them about an occasion when I first took over the pub, during the transition period where the retiring publican was still showing me the ropes. A few weeks before, a small cyclone has torn down the telephone wires, and the lines had put up a jury-rig which was a bit slack where it crossed the Annan River. When a big tide came in the wires hung so low that they went into the water and you couldn't ring up because if you did it shorted out the line.

Around that time a bloke came in by car to the pub and asked if he could ring up Cooktown to get a mechanic out to fix his car, which was playing up a bit. The retiring publican says, "Just hang on a minute while I check," and pulls out a tide chart and start to study it. This makes the bloke stare at him hard. He doesn't say anything except you can see he weighing things up a bit. The Irishman and I are there and while the publican is studying the tide chart, this bloke asks the Irishman what's the weather going to do. Without a word the Irishman hands him the phone book, meaning of course that he should ring up the Weather Bureau at the same time if he wanted the real story, but the bloke doesn't interpret it this way at all.

I had been studying a bit of racing form in a Miller's Guide while this exchange was going on, and I saw him give a quick look at the Guide in my hand. I can see it suddenly occur to him that he's landed right in the middle of a self-contained funny farm. Then the publican asked, "What month is it?" and I being a smartarse, replied, "What month do you normally plant lettuce?"

This was too much for the bloke, and he let out a moaning

"Ooooh Keriist" and bolted for the car followed by a cackle of laughter from me which could only have been interpreted as being maniacal . . . which perhaps it was.

We had to send the women out to pacify him and convince him that we weren't that mad. Finally he unlocked the car door and came in to make his phone call, as the tide *was* low and he *could* ring up. You could see he still treated us with a certain amount of reserve, wondering perhaps if the women had only smoothed things over a bit so we wouldn't get violent.

I told you we had a special brand of eccentricity up here, but luckly it is of a less virulent strain than they have in Canberra. The audience all says they'd have liked to have seen the act, but I say you can't now as they've raised the wires again to the correct height.

The two birds are enjoying everything, and the jokers with them also. The old bloke has been trying to get a word in, but has been unable to up to now. I know what he wants to talk about . . . Palmer Kate's jo-mo, but I'm trying to edge him of this subject as I know if he gets fair dinkum he'll probably get me in as well. And I know also there's no way you could hold de Valera's protégé out on a deal like this.

He sidles round the direct approach by asking me first of all, "What about that other dame? You know, the Grecian Bend."

I say she wasn't nearly as famous as the other one and she liked the turps too much to ever get on. As my wife always says you can't drink and run a business as well, but I always tell her this isn't a business . . . it's just a way of life.

The old bloke wants to know if the Grecian Bend went in for this fancy bedroom-ware like Palmer Kate.

"No," I say, "she just went down and got a straight custom-built enamel job off the hook at Donald and Blacks." Then I tell them about how one night she got "off her bike" with a client and pelted a few naughty words after him as he departed, *and* her current utensil as well. She couldn't find the thing the next day and had to go down to get a replacement job. Down at the store they had them hung up on nails on rafters along with the teapots, billy cans and other tinware. The storekeeper has to fish them off with the hooks with a thing like a boathook but not so sturdy. When he was lowering this very necessary bit of stock in trade on the end of this boathook thing, it slipped off and came down crash on the head of the Lady Mayoress who was also in the shop. She put on a real act over it, and threatened to have all the houses closed up. The vote went against it mainly because they didn't have any women councillors those days.

I had often heard about people getting up on a throne to be crowned, but this was the first time I heard of anyone getting crowned by a throne. It busted up the artificial fruit salad which the old dragon was wearing on her hat at the time, and she threatened to sue but didn't.

I think the act was mainly caused by a current of underlying jealousy just the same. The only one to suffer of course was the poor old Mayor who not only got a great tongue bashing but had to cough up for a new hat as well.

One young fellow says, "What did they call her the Grecian Bend for?" I explain to him that this was a shape women managed to get themselves into those days, which looked like something out of a modernistic painting. It was all exaggerated by the addition of a thing called a bustle which was a sort of rear bumper bar. The more the women managed to get into this particular Bend style, the more they looked as thought they had been hit in the middle of the back with a slip rail.

The old bloke wants to get back to the subject of old Palmer Kate, and the possibility of recovering the Golden Vessel. He harks back to that and says, "Do you really think the thing is still in existence?"

"I think it must be, because it was so well known . . . by the male population anyway. It would be hard for anyone to fence it if it'd been stolen, and so far there's no record of it going into the melting pot. If it was already in someone's antique art collection, they'd be skiting about it now.

"Of course," I say, "it could have been smuggled out of the country. Maybe it's in some pervy old lord's collection in London and he's just keeping it to himself."

I can see the old bloke is working up to suggesting the formation of a syndicate to go hunting for this fabulous relic. He's a bit worried-looking, as he tells me there's a crowd out there already looking for cave paintings on the old Palmer track. He's certain if they got to hear of it they'd abandon their present pursuit and get on the trail of the real thing. I reassure him on this, as I explain to him that this bunch really are only concerned with murri paintings.

Well, the upshot of it is that he says, "Look. I'd be willing to put in a few dollars for this project, and I think the others would be too."

"Ok," I say. "I knew this would happen. I could feel it in me water. How much is the entrance fee?"

He says a couple of dollars, and Irish pipes up and says, "Not enough. Make it ten dollars."

The old bloke says he doesn't mind putting in ten dollars, but I say listen this is only for a start. We have to search the records first other wise we might be going on a wild goose chase. I think we ought to put in only two dollars each until we find out a bit more authentic information about it."

They all agree on this, and I get out some paper and a biro and start to draw up a sort of ship's articles and crew list.

I say we'll have to register the formation of the syndicate with the Attorney-General to make it valid. Also we'll have to write to the Crown Law Office to see if we own the bloody thing when we find it or wether we have to hand it over to the National Trust.

The Irishman says, "Arrgh, all the money will be taken up in stamps and stationery soon, and there won't even be a deposit left to put on a good sort of packhorse let alone a pack saddle." Well the girls have their two dollar bills ready and the two young jokers too, but the Irishman is still fingering a ten dollar bill.

I can see he's going to be a bit stubborn, so I start writing out the crew list and putting "$2 Pd." after each name and then adding their addresses after it so we can contact them again. I explain to them this is only a down payment as it'll cost a lot more to carry on later. It may come to a hundred dollars each, but they all say they don't mind and they'll put the balance in on call. We now have fourteen dollars in kitty, but we'll probably need $1400 if we're going to do things right on the safari with the present price of grog, especially as I will be supplying the grog.

Irish reluctantly puts two dollars in, but I can see he wants to go for things in a big way, just like old Palmer Kate did. After all, he says, this is the One and Only of its kind in the world and should be worth a bundle. He says you could ask a squillion for it at least, so why be so lousy in the first place. He points out that it has utility as well as artistic value attached to it. We ought to be able to sell it for a big figure to one of those wealthy Hollywood movie stars, especially as it's already broke in. However, he's fighting a losing battle in trying to get the mob to put more in just now, so he settles for another stubby.

I say, "Of course if we find it, we'll have to get a new packsaddle built for it too, to make the thing really authentic, and they cost as much today as what the old convience would've cost when it came of the workbench."

We decide to call the safari Operation PKGP, which sounds like a secret police outfit but isn't. It means Palmer Kate's Golden Pot, and we decide to go on the trip in August when it open season for black ducks. Another thing, the barrimundi start to bite about then, so we should be able to live high while we're on the Golden Quest. We also decide that we'll have to go by four-wheel vehicle, as we'd want a long string of packhorses to handle all the grog we need to make the trip a success.

Another car pulls up just then with a couple of tin scratchers in it, so all further discussion of Operation PKGP has to cease and I hurriedly remove the articles of agreement and crew list.

The tin scratchers walk into the bar and one bloke says, "VB. g'day," and the other bloke says, "Fourex. How are yer?"

So I set 'em up, and since Irish knows these blokes he starts a round of introduction. The rest of of them hook into their stubbies, and there's plenty of talk and scraping of bar stools to make a bit more room. The talk gets onto tin. These two jokers say they'd have done much better this time only their chainsaw broke down. They couldn't keep the timber back from the open-cut face, and all the trees had fallen in on them and caused a hell of a mess. They say if they'd only kept their old peg-tooth crosscut saw they'd have been better off. They reckon they could cut more timber with a crosscut any day of the week.

"What would you know about cutting timber," says Irish, "you're tin scratchers."

"I cut a lot of timber in me time."

"Where did you cut timber?"

"In the Sahara Forest," says the bloke.

One of the young fellow pipes up and says there's no timber in the Sahara, it's a desert.

"I don't know what it's like now," says this bloke quietly, "but there was plenty timber there when I first started on it."

I can see that this yarn has got the Irishman intrigued. Of course he'd fall for anything, as I know he's got a sheet of sandpaper in his private effects which he treasure, thinking it's a map of the Sahara Desert with the waterholes marked in secret code which he is trying to figure out.

"How's your new pump working?" said Irish.

"Orright except for the eels. Every so often we have to stop the pump and take a batch of eels out of the impeller."

"Why don't you put a screen over your suction?"

"S'easier to take the plate off the side of the pump than to go diving in bloody cold water," says the bloke. "Besides, this way you get your breakfast as well — except we're getting a bit fed up with jellied eels. Still I'll admit it's a nice change from bandicoot."

One of the girls says, "Why don't you try eating the eels some other way, instead of having jellied eel all the time?"

"Listen miss, these eels are already jellied when we get 'em from being whirled around inside the pump for a while. Anyway, it's good for you. They reckon fish food is brain food. Actually me mate here is so silly I sometimes think he ought to start in on a whale."

His mate says he not that silly, as he know you couldn't snig a whale up the bush track to their camp. And besides, what would you do with the left overs?

While this exchange is going on, I see two pollution trails spearing down the hill, but I can't see what's causing them. Shortly afterwards a couple of weirdos arrive on Hondas, and after extracting themselves from the deck cargo, they ease themselves into the bar, leather jackets and all. They say, "G'day," and order up a couple of stubbies.

Irish asks them where they're headed, or don't they know. They say they're going up to Cape York but aren't sure of the correct route. Irish says, "Ask the boss here, he'll probably put you wise."

They turn to me for directions, and I tell them it's not hard to find your way up the Peninsula, as from here on she tapers into a point. All you have to do is to keep the east coast on your right, and the overland telegraph on your left and you can't miss. I say they'll know when they come to Cape York as there's a sort of a big waterhole there which they call Torres Strait.

"How deep is this Torres Strait?" says one bloke and I tell them it's not very deep. You could walk across to New Guinea if you roll your strides up except for one bit of a gutter where they take the tankers through.

"But we're not going to New Guinea!"

"Well, were are you going?" says Irish.

"We were trying to keep it a bit secret," one fellow answers, and I can see a livening of interest all along the bar as the mob has a strong suspicion these jokers might've got onto to the idea of old Kate's legacy. Irish renews his attracts on them to find out the object of their trip.

"Well, look," says one of the bikies finally, "it's like this. Me mate and I have been reading about all these 'firsts'; like Amy Johnson who was the first woman to fly solo from England to Australia, Kingsford Smith the first to fly the Pacific, Lindberg the first to fly the Atlantic, you know the sort of thing."

They've got us all on edge waiting for the disclosure. We're wondering what bastardry they're contemplating. One bloke takes a deep breath and we hang on his first words like a mob at Doomben after a photo waiting for the numbers to go up.

"It's like this. We're going to ride the bikes up to Cape York overland, and then we're going to ride south again along the Barrier Reef. Don't you think that would be a good 'first'?"

Who do these blokes think they're dealing with? Irish and me are black belt yarn spinners, so we play along.

"Take a few spare tyres with you," says Irish, not fazed at all, "plenty of puncture repair outfits. You'll have to ride through a few thousand acres of crown of thorns starfish, and we find the thorns are bloody deadly on tyres."

"The best time to try it is on neap tides when the water just laps the top of the coral wall all day," I say. "Any other time you have to ride through a bit of water, and it'll rust the spokes of your wheels."

One of the girls chips in and says, "Why didn't you get one of those big motorcycle manufacturers to sponsor the trip?"

They say they already have done this, and that one crowd has promised them brand new models when they finish the trip. Also the Tourist Bureau is going to advertise it as a round trip and put little rest areas all along the reef where you can pull over and sleep for the night. Then they settle down a bit and want to know more about the trip up the Peninsula. They reckon they've got the it all worked out as far as the Barrier Reef trip is concerned, it being impossible to get lost on it, but the trip north is a bit different, having trees and swamps and things to get slewed in.

They ask me if there are any deep rivers to cross and wether the crocodiles are dangerous. I tell them the only big river is the Normanby. They'll have a bit of trouble crossing it, as they'll have to wade over waist deep and push the Hondas and dry them out afterwards.

They say, "What about the crocs while were crossing this river?" and I say not to worry at all about the crocs as the tiger sharks have cleaned them all out.

"I suppose your sponsors gave you a bit of silver for the road eh?" says the Irishman.

They get the message and buy a round of drinks. Then after that, thinking they might get full enough for us to divert them from their purpose, they get ready to leave again. They get final instructions from me about the route, and I say, "It's quiet simple. Just remember, east coast on the right, telegraph line on the left. You can't mistake this; it's like a big, long clothes line with a prop about every 100 yards."

Then they go out and clamber onto their Nipponese stock horses, put the spurs in and the steeds take off, kicking stones into the bar as usual.

After they have gone there is quiet for a while, then the old blokes says, "I think their bloody well mad."

I can see everyone is a bit relieved that these idiots are going on a scatterbrain journey like they propose, and aren't interested in a straight-out sensible treasure hunt like we have in mind.

After a while one of the young fellows tells me that as they were coming out of Cooktown they saw a peculiar thing . . . a monkey riding a big dog chasing a wild pig. For a start they weren't sure if their eyes were playing tricks on them, but as they all saw the same thing, it must be true.

"It's true enough all right," I said. "There's and old chap in there who has a snakery full of taipans and pythons and death adders and he uses the monkey dog act just before he milks the tiapans. They gallop round and round outside the cages and the snakes get dizzy following them. Of course the dog and monkey get dizzy too and that's how they wind up out on the road chasing pigs.

"One local cattleman, when he saw the act for the first time, went off the grog for a week until someone told him it was fair dinkum. But there's a funnier act than that around Cooktown. A bloke there has a pet pig that goes pig hunting.

"When he goes out with his dogs to hunt wild pig, the pet pig, which was reared with dogs and thinks it's one too, goes along as well — the dirty traitor — and the trouble is to avoid shooting the wrong pig. Sometime in the melee all the dogs fasten onto the pet pig and the wild one escapes and the pet pig won't talk to the dogs for a week afterwards."

The talk drifts back to the Palmer gold rush again and they are still on this line of talk when old Bill, a scratcher from the hills, drifts in. He joins in about the Palmer, and says he was in the rush. "I was out there when the blacks were bad."

The old bloke tells them about getting croc skins on the Gulf shores. There used to be plenty there out on the saltpans, and he got them by shapening small sticks each end. When the croc went to grab him, he just put the sharpened stick between the brute's jaw and when he clamped on it, you had him, although you had to watch out he didn't woodend you with his tail. He says he had to give it up on the saltpans. Though, as he ran out of wood to make his croc spreaders. In any case, it was all gofer wood.

"What's gofer wood?" says one chap.

"They call it gofer wood because you have to go fer miles to get it."

One day he was after barramundi, and sat down on a log and fished for a while. Something took his bait, so he cut up another bit of bait. When he finished, he struck his croc-skinning knife into the log. The log gave a heave and headed for the water. It was then he found out that the log was a big croc he'd been after for months. He couldn't shoot anymore crocs until he killed this fellow — and got his knife back.

"What did your wife do to fill in time when you were away on the croc hunts?" says one bloke.

"Never had a wife," says old Bill. "Don't believe in 'em."

"What're you so crooked on wives for, Bill?"

"Arrgh," says the old fellow, a man has to give half his tucker away to get the other half cooked." which is sound reasoning and should be taken into account when a man is battling.

Just then an old murri appears like a wraith at the window of the speakeasy. Without saying anything, he quietly puts down some change and I go in and bring him out a stubby. While I knocking the head off it, the old fellow scans the bar with a look on his face which is half smile and half maniacal leer. I can see some of the customers are a bit worried about the way he looks at them. I reassure them saying that the old fellow is a bit mad, but not violent. Some mug pipes up and says, "What sent him mad?" I explain that about two Christmases back someone gave him a new boomerang, and the poor bastard went made trying to throw the old one away. I tell them that the only time I put him in the dog house is when he's a bit short of change.

"Oh, you have a dog house here too, eh?" says someone

"Yeah," I say, "the biggest in the world you're in it when you're out of the pub."

"Where does the old fellow live, and what does he live on?"

"He has a bit of a gunya down by the river. He gets Social Security — he calls it 'choshull' — but he reserves this for grog. Most of the time he does pretty well on native tucker which you can't buy with money. He usually has a bit of goanna tail for breakfast. This is not only a pretty satisfying meal, but after you've sucked all the meat off the bones, you can play it like a Jew's-harp and get a fair sort of tune out of it — that is if you're musically inclined."

As I said before, it's known as overland trout, and not unlike fish to eat; in fact when we were a bit short of tucker at the pub one Easter, we rung it in as the fish course on Good Friday. Sometimes the old murri had the presence of mind to buy a bit of flour before his "choshull" runs out, and he bakes himself a damper or two when he can't get onto a goanna or a nice fat carpet snake.

All the time this chit-chat is going on there's a steady slurping sound from the stubby drinkers, with me knocking heads off a new round any time I see them empty, which is an automatic reflex with me. When they first brought out those patent stubby coolers which are just a plastic overcoat for a stubby and don't cool it a bit, I naturally brought a few of them to try. I soon woke up to their failings, the main one of course being that you can't see the state of the tide, to see if anyone is dragging the chain. I determined to get rid of the lot of them, but soon realised I wouldn't have to do a thing to dispose of them, just let nature take its course. In no time at all the light-fingered and forgetful had done the job for me.

Just then the local taxi pulls up and disgorges a couple of tourist who turn out to be Chinese. The taxi bloke's name is Richard Sincock — we automatically call him Evil Dick. I can see his customers are gentlemen by their Bond Street clobber. (None of those two-hour slap-up jobs from Hong Kong for them.)

The Irishman takes it on himself to be a one-man welcoming party, shooing the rest of the crowd further along the bar like a mob of fowls, to make room for the newcomers. He introduces himself with a heavy handshakes. The Chinamen respond with beaming smiles which disclose the gobful of gold teeth that look like the inner vaults of Fort Knox.

Evil Dick comes in and wedges himself on a high stool and says, "Give me a Fourex. I don't know what these gentlemen are going to have."

The Irishman is trying to make introductions all round, with some measure of success. I am impatient to get the orders and finally elicit the information that they'd like beer. I grab a couple of stubbies of Pipeline and behead them, having the presence of mind to put down a couple of glasses as well. I'm not sure wether these blokes have been properly trained to drink stubbies. Between a lot of bowing and hissing and more vague introductions, they manage to pour a beer for themselves and take a sip or two as well as a sniff or two, to see if the foreign devils have loaded the drinks with a dash of strychnine.

The Irishman says, "What did you say your name was again?" and one bloke admits to the name of Chow Mein. The Irishman says that's a type of Chinese tucker you eat in the cities when you get full of grog, but this joker says it's also a Chinese name.

"What do you blokes do for a living, mate?" says Irish, and this bloke says he is in the Chinese Red Airforce, and he's on holiday taking a world cruise. Irish wants to know what he is in the airforce, and he admits to being a pilot and adds quietly, "Suicide pilot."

"How can you be a suicide pilot and still be alive?"

The bloke says he hasn't had a go yet, but he's been trained for it. The Irishman isn't too happy with this explantation, and I'm starting to get a bit suspicious myself. I'll bet these two jokers are Taiwanese, trying to put one over us. Maybe that bugger Evil Dick has put 'em up to it. Irish says on the side his name should be Chicken Chow Mien.

The other Chinaman admits to being a pilot also, but only as a stunt flyer. The Irishman grabs hold of this quickly and says, "I bet your name will be Wun Wing Low."

Anyway, I decided it's about time I rescued them from the clutches of this Sinn Feiner, and I bring out a few tin samples and such like to get things back to normal, although the normal state in this bar verges on the abnormal from anywhere else.

The Chinamen want to take a few pictures and when I say it's OK, they both fly out of the bar to the taxi and come back hunchbacked under the weight of the cameras slung around their necks. This is a signal for the Irishman to shoot through, which he does very effectively by going to a place the call the men's room in some places, and the toilet in others, but up here it is known as the shithouse. I wonder about this. Maybe he's allergic to cameras. He's sure adverse to getting his mug shot on celluliod and I doubt it's because he's concerned about breaking the lens.

The visitors take a number of shots inside and outside the bar and are very careful to get good shots of a stuffed frill-necked lizard on the wall which looks something like a dragon. I suspect that with a bit of trick photography later they'll blow it up and superimpose their own brave persons onto the final print to big note themselves at home, dragons having a sort of Number One priority in China.

By now the Irishman judges correctly that the photography session is over, and having gained a new thirst from his visit out back, comes boldly into the bar again and says, "Fill 'em up all round," but the alleged protégés of old Mousey Tongue won't hear of it. They demand that they be allowed to shout which they do after a few feeble objections are lodged.

I line them up as the last head falls, one of the visitors says, "You will pleos join us too in having a drink," but I'm already in front of them, and quietly hold up my stubby for their inspection.

I had also put the old murri in the round as well, and he's grimacing and making funny faces at the Chinamen, all in a spirit of good fellowship, but I can see that all is not well with the visitors. Perhaps they think that the show the old murri is putting on is only a prelude to an attack. Possible they feel that at any moment the old fellow will grab a bunch of shovel-nose spears and go into a violent action. You can't very well blame them, as this is probably the first murri with whom they've even had a passing contact. Probably remembering the stories handed down from their grandfathers from the Palmer days, they are keeping a bright eye on the old bird.

The grog is finally starting to work right through to the finger tips of the clientele, and there's a steady buzz of noise (sometimes called conversation) in the bar. I see on of the Chinamen casting an appraising eye over one of the birds, but they're both too tightly ringed in for him to make much progress.

Finally the taxi driver reminds them that they'll have to get going if they're to catch their plane on schedule, so after sucking down the last of their stubbies, they depart with numerous little bows and scraping of the feet.

Just then my wife comes into the bar with a tray of cold chicken legs and wings for counter lunch. The Irishman puts up the most sensible suggestion that we "line 'em up again", which is the sort of language I subscribe to any day of the week. My wife departs with a warning not to be feeding the bones to the dogs as, she'll do that at the right time, and not to forget to give the old murri a bit as well. I'm up against this as I don't want to spoil his taste for goanna and carpet snake by feeding him on chicken, but he gets his quota just the same.

Well, I behead a line-up of stubbies, and we get stuck into what's left of the chicken after the young fellows and birds have zeroed in on it. It's the only time for hours that there hasn't been a noise like a stirred beehive in the bar. It doesn't take them long to guzzle down the tucker, and the Irishman, being very level headed, dribbles out of both sides of his mouth at once. I'd bar this bloody bog trotter from the premises, except as I said before, I'd lose twenty-five percent of my trade and half my entertainment. I sometimes wonder why he doesn't claim me as a dependant for income tax purposes. I will admit he hunts a bit of trade out of the bar, but there are times when this is no loss.

The week before my dog broke his chain and went bush, and the Irishman said, "I'll get you a good chain. One that he won't break in a hurry," and he went down to a junk heap at the back and came back dragging a fairly heavy snigging chain.

A tin scratcher who he didn't get on too well with took the opportunity to have a crack at him as he dragged the chain along saying, "Running to true form eh? Dragging the chain as usual. What are you dragging the chain for, Irish?"

The Irishman took this in his stride with a quick retort, "Listen mug, you ever try to *push* one of these?" The drinks were on the tin scratcher who conceded defeat in the verbal exchange anyway.

One of the birds was harking back to the visit of the two Chinese gentlemen, and mentioned that one of them had promised to send her a picture of the bar and everyone in it. I said this was only a lurk to get her address, but she said no, because he was going to send it care of the pub and I would then have to forward it to her. She said she couldn't see how one photo could show all the bar at the same time.

"Didn't you see that big camera he had, with the fish-eye lens in it?"

She asks what a fish-eye lens is, and I explain that it is a special lens which can look all *round* you and not at you like a Murri's* eye that can look all around you without looking at you. That was how he could take a shot of all the bar at once, which was a good enough explanation of a scientific marvel.

The other bird says they had a good time in Cooktown, and that a new café had opened up. You can get real good meals now as the bloke running it is a mighty cook and everything he cooks is done to perfection. In fact, she says, he can cook eggs like nobody else can.

Old Bill the tin scratcher clears his throat a couple of times and grunts, "Well, he must be cooking them on *edge*."

I don't like too much of this talk about things you can eat,

* Murri. A contraction of Murribumah, which means a native male in the Cooktown dialect.

and steer the talk back into other channels and suggest we have something to drink instead. There must be something else in life to drink besides beer, bloody beer all the bloody time. The Irishman agrees with me, and as it's the old bloke's shout, we all ram for a change of drinks. After that the rest of them order up all sorts of queer concoctions which I know I have no hope of producing.

I turn to the bog trotter and ask his preference. He names a Northern Territory Impossibility, which turns out to be a dry gin in milk.

I ask him what sort of milk he wants and he says it doesn't matter whether it's pasteurised, or homogenised or buggerised, as long as it's milk.

I tell him I'll have to round up a passing cow to get the milk, so he had better take his gin now, and drink the milk straight later on when I get it.

They all order up some hard tack or other and one bloke wants rum negrito; so I say to him that he must have been in New Guinea at one time, and he says, "Yes, how did you know?"

I tell him that I used to think this stuff was some sort of a tropical disease, and later on when I went up to Port Moresby one time, I found out it was . . . they all drink it up there. But, I said, it's not incurable. We had a bloke come down from Port Moresby once and he was in a bad way (he'd been there just a little bit too long). After we beat all the Little Men off his shoulders with a bat, we saved him by putting him on a controlled diet of 33 OP, straight from the well-head in Bundaberg. Ah well, every man to his own brand of poison.

5

Sometimes I feel that the job is getting too much for me and I'm sorely tempted to apply for another job. Say, Harbour Master, Ayers Rock, for instance, or Chief Fisheries Inspector, Birdsville, although a man might get just a little bit *too* dehydrated out there. I can't stand any of these really hot places.

Like Normanton for instance. I was talking to a bloke from there recently, and he said it was that hot there one day he saw two dogs chasing a cat . . . and they were *all* walking.

The crowd is drinking merrily on, when a bloke comes out from Cooktown in the Holden with his wife and kids and pulls into the pub for a quick beer. We ask him where he is headed and he says he is going through to Cairns as there's a circus in town down there, and the kids have hounded him into going to see it. He reckons he's going to take his tribe round to the monkeys' cage, mainly to impress on the monkeys how easy *they* get it, even if they are locked up most of the time.

Somebody chips in and asks old Bill the tin scratcher if he's ever been to a circus, and he says, "Yeah, once in nineteen-o-four. A circus came up to Cooktown on the coastal boat, and I went to it. Never again though."

"Why didn't you go again, Bill?" asks the man with the tribe.

"Arrgh, they don't play fair," says Bill. "There's a big bloke called Captain Something, but why they called him Captain I don't know, as they didn't have a boat. He's got a rigout on him that's a cross between a black tracker's uniform and a Tibetan admiral's. He gets into a steel cage with a couple of mangy-looking old lions that looked as though they were going to die any time from malnutrition. This bloke starts to annoy the lions, whippin' 'em on the arse with a dirty big stockwhip, and pokin' them in the eye with the leg of a chair, and makin' them sit up on a stool to beg, and jumping 'em through hoops and all that. The old lions cop all this without protest as they think there might be a bit of feed hanging on the end of it all. But the big bloke is too mean to give them a bite to eat after doing all these tricks, and they could've eaten a bullock between them (something that would dress out a six or seven hundred), bones and all.

"To make matters worse this big captain bloke pulls out a dirty big Peacemaker colt and fires a couple of shots at 'em. Then he starts to whip 'em on the arse again and tries to herd 'em back into a small cage without giving them a bite to eat. Just keeps annoyin' the poor bastards with the whip and the chair legs, and lettin' the Peacemaker off right in their faces.

"The next thing you know, one of the lions does his block. He'd *had* this bloke, and he makes a swipe at him and knocks him out cold . . . I don't blame him for it either. Another urger belonging to the circus races in with a Winchester 44 rifle and drops the old lion cold. Then the other lion hops back into the small cage quick and lively, in case it gets a dose of lead too. That was enough for me. I left the show then, because I reckoned it was a low act to shoot the poor bloody lion. They should have shot the lion tamer, as he started it all. No, they don't play fair at all."

Then the Irishman chips in and says, "They should have taken the Peacemaker and the whip off the big bloke and given them to the other lion, and let the lion put him through the hoops by way of variety. I know the lion couldn't very well use the whip or the revolver, but he could've made heavy grunting sounds and chopping noises around the seat of the captain's jodhpurs. That'd be one way to put the captain through the hoop. The mob would have enjoyed the act a bit more too."

I wonder why these circus managers don't catch onto this act. Of course we know that it wouldn't work, because lions generally are not sadistic.

Just then a joker comes in to the pub from up Rossville way. He's a sort of semi-retired bloke who gets a bit of a pension like most of them do up there. We call the joint Pensionville. He struggles along on this and runs a few chooks as well; sells a few eggs and an odd fowl or two to keep going. He comes into the pub and takes up a barrier position and grunts, "Rum," which I have anticipated anyway.

He looks real haggard and I think for a minute he might be going into Cooktown to give himself up to the doctor. I say,"You look a bit crook, mate," and he says no, he's OK. Just a bit tired, that's all.

I say it might be something to do with this energy crisis we read about, although we've always had an energy crisis in this area. Most of the bludgers round here have only just got enough energy to crawl to the pub and down a few stubbies. If ever it comes about that they can't manage to do that, there'll be a real energy crisis.

"Do you want to buy a few chooks?" he says to me then.

"How many you got?"

"About twenty-five."

I tell him that we have enough chooks ourselves but the missus might be interested in a few killers.

"You don't have to kill these, as they're already killed and dressed."

Naturally I'm curious, and ask him if he's going out of business with the chooks, but he says no. This stunt was a sort of accident; really a sort of chain reaction, that got all these chooks killed at once. By now I'm all ears, and so is the rest of the mob in the bar.

"What happened, mate?" says the Irishman.

"Well, it's a long story."

We all hang on his words now, thinking he might have gone a bit queer, to go and kill twenty-five chooks at once, but he's the sort of joker you can't hurry. He sucks his rum down quietly, and we wait for him to unfold the tale, as it's no good trying to bustle him. The Irishman exhibits his usual impatience and says, "How did it happen, mate?"

"I told you it was a long story — really a chain reaction."

"Yeah," I said. "You said that before." I'm starting to squirm a bit too, as he's taking so long to get into gear.

"Well," he says, "you know how bad the snakers are up my way?" and we chip in and say, "Yeah."

"About every second night a man's got to get out of bed, get the old Greener pumpgun, and go and blast one of the crawling bastards in the fowl house. Well, last night I hear the fowls squawking so I get up and scratch around to find the gun. I'm still in my nightshirt see, and I don't bother to get changed because I know if I don't get out there pretty soon, the bloody snake will have half the flock dead. You know how it is with those black-headed pythons; they'll kill the bloody lot before they start to eat one."

"Yeah. We know that," chips in the Irishman. "Let's hear the story."

"I'm trying to tell the yarn if you'd only listen."

"Yeah, yeah, go on."

"Well," he says, "some people might call it a sequence of events, but I call it a chain reaction."

"You said that before," says Irish.

"Shut up, you bog-trotting bastard. Let the man tell the story."

"Well," goes on the old bloke, "I get the torch then and the battery is so weak I nearly have to strike a match to see if the bloody thing is shining. I've got no other battery anyhow, so this'll have to do and out I go — still in my nightshirt — peering around the wirenetting, looking for this blasted snake. I see half a dozen chooks already dead on the floor of the chook house, and there's the snake swallowing one having already got another one down. Well, you know that dirty big alsation dog I've got? He's followed me out, deciding he's got to be in the act too."

"I thought this was a snake yarn — not a shaggy dog story," says the Irishman.

We all howl him down, to let the old bloke get on with his chain-reaction story.

"Well," he says, "I'm just drawing a bead on the snake with the pumpgun, and I'm bending down a bit to get the snake in a better position, when that bloody dog of mine sticks his cold nose right where he shouldn't, and the shock is too much for me. I pull both triggers at once and blast a couple of dozen chooks into eternity. If I'd had another cartridge I'd have shot the bloody dog too, I was that mad."

He takes time off now to down another rum which I have providentially put in front of him.

"That's how I come to be so worn out today — sittin' up all night pluckin' and guttin' fowls. You can see now why I say it was a sort of chain reaction."

Silence for a while, then somebody says, "Did you get the snake?"

"Yeah," he says, "but not right away. I didn't have another cartridge handy, but I would see he was already more or less in gaol and couldn't get away. He'd eaten a couple of chooks, and with the bulge in the middle he was too big to get back out through the wire netting. I left him there and got on with the job of pluckin' chooks. He's still there. I'm going to ring up that bloke with the snakery in Cooktown to see if he wants him."

I say it's not a bad sort of a yarn, and ask him to have a rum on me on the strength of it. He gets so insulted about the implication that it's a yarn that he bloody near knocks back the rum. However, to placate him, I say we'll buy a dozen of the chooks, providing he doesn't charge for the weight of lead in them as well. *And* I tell him, we don't want any of those that the snake pulverised first. The Irishman says at least the snake-killed ones would be tender anyway, but if I want to tenderise a chook I don't want any assistance from a python. We haven't got that serious an energy crisis here yet.

This starts a spate of snake stories, but I won't be in any of these made-up yarns . . . only the fair dinkum ones. So I tell them about the bloke out at Laura who'd been on the grog so long, and was in such a bad way, that the publican put the Dog Act on him. He got so desperate for a drink, he broke into the school one weekend and drunk all the spirits out of the bottled specimens of taipans and death adders and king brown's heads which they had there to explain to the kids what bitey-biteys look like. *That's* what I call *real* snake juice. If he could've only got a bit of it into him beforehand, he could've crawled into the school, instead of breaking into the joint. But he crawled *out*, and the school's not far from the cop shop. As he happened to crawl in that direction, the Sergeant just left the door of the calaboose open and he gave himself up, thinking he was crawling into the pub door. The Sergeant said it was the easiest pinch he'd ever made. Look — no hands! But he had to go and buy half a gallon of metho, to pour over the specimens so they wouldn't get on ' the bugle'.

The school teacher was quite pleased about it as he said you could now see the specimens quite clearly . . . the old embalming fluid had got a bit murky. The old deadbeat must've reckoned it was a powerful brew, for the first couple of slugs anyway. After that it would have tasted like century-old Madeira.

The snake yarns and the drinking go on at about equal rates. I don't mind this providing there's a fair return for the hours a man has to put in and the amount of bullshit that a man has to put up with. A new arrival comes into the bar and he looks real crook. He doesn't know what to order, so I ask him what he's been drinking. He says, "Everything on the shelf. I've got a terrible hangover," so I tell him the best thing is a hair of the dog that bit him. He asks the Irishman what he does for a hangover, but Irish says he never gets one.

"Gee, how do you manage to avoid getting a hangover?" he says.

"I just *stay* stoned," says the Irishman with a grin. "If by any chance I do feel a bit seedy, I just have rum and more."

"What's more?" says the bloke.

"More rum."

He says on one occasion when he went up into the hills to his tin mine, he took another joker up with him for a bit of company. But not knowing this bloke's capacity, he miscalculated the amount of turps to take up and they had a dreadful experience of running out of grog. The Irishman got real crook. This bloke he'd taken up with him was a New Zealander, and he looked after the Irishman during the bad period and nursed him back to health. He said to this bloke, "You know what, mate, you're the only really decent Kiwi I've ever met. I'm of two minds; whether to let you go, or to shoot you now . . . just to stop you going bad." He wondered why the bloke never would go back up to camp with him again.

I've mixed up a good sort of concoction for this joker with the hangover by this, putting in just about everything of high voltage that I can lay my hands on, following the kill or cure system. I reckon if he can only get this charge down, he'll be so roten instantly that he'll only imagine he's got a hangover.

He hooks the heart starter into him. He goes purple round the gills, and both his eyes bulge out of their sockets sideways. He sits frozen like that for a while, then his eyeballs slowly turn frontwards again.

"How did that go down, mate?" says the Irishman. "Feel a bit better now?"

The bloke gives a brave grin, and tries to say, "It didn't hurt a bit", but he can't get his vocal cords fully coordinated.

The Irishman says to him, "Why don't you get onto these new Get Smart Pills?"

The bloke has recovered his faculties just enough to mumble, "Where do you get them?" and the big-hearted Irish bastard says he has a few, and he can try them. This joker falls for this lot. I know that what the Irishman has is a few goats' pills in a paper packet, which he had collected from a farmhouse a mile or so from the pub, goats' pills being the end product from a goat's digestive tract. They are called pills because of their distinctive size and shape, and are just one of nature's many humorous varieties of waste disposal. Unlike nuclear wastes these are soluble.

Irish produces the packet and says to the bloke, "Go on. Get 'em into you."

The blokes says, "Are they effective?" and Irish says they work striaght away. So the bloke tosses one down and then starts to nibble another one. All of a sudden a strange look comes over his face, and he says to Irish, "Listen you dirty bastard. These are goats; pills."

"There you are," says Irish. "They work, don't they? You're getting smart already."

However the bloke finally takes it in good part after the Irishman has brought him a stubby to take the taste out of his mouth, and the atmosphere settles back to normal; that is, normal for the Den.

A big tin scrather bloke bulges his way into the bar just then, and demands a stubby of VB. This bloke is built like the proverbial brick-out house. I know that he and the Irishman just don't see eye to eye, except on the rare occasions when they get locked in mortal combat.

After a few preliminary skirmishes wherein a few extremely rude remarks pass between them, I don't need a crystal ball to see that not only are there rumours of war, but every likelihood of full hostilities breaking out. I try to engage this big mug in conversation to divert him from the inevitable clash with the Son of Erin.

However, it does no good because, although he's not what you call a troublemaker, he always seems to drag a fair batch of it around with him. I can see at a glance he is a bit niggly, which is nearly a normal state of affairs with him.

Times goes on, and a few more stubbies are sunk all round with the Irishman and the big tin scratcher hurling abuse at each other, and me ducking my head a bit so I don't get caught too much in the crossfire. I go in to get a new round of the drinks for the mob, and the next thing the start of open hostilities is heralded by the usual loud clanging of bar stools

KANGAROOSTERS

Often seen around the Lion's Den

on concrete, and head of four letter words mixed up with animal-like grunts.

I come back quickly into the bar to find the big bloke remodelling the Irishman's face. He doesn't mind this really, as he knows that any alteration can only be an improvement. The wise drinkers waste no time in vacating the bar; not so much to give the combatants a fair go, as to preserve their own hides. They take up suitable vantage points from which to observe the slaughter, and at the same time to barrack for the bloke they think is going to win. As I think I said before (if I didn't I'm saying it now), the Irishman can't fight real good, but he takes a hell of a lot of killing.

I pull out a civilising agent I have under the bar, known as a bung starter, which is a dirty big mallet, a hangover from the days when *real* beer used to come up here in *real* wooden kegs and which was used to get to tap in and out of the keg. I've made an improvement to the original model, by fitting a longer handle to it made out of a big lawyer cane, to give me more reach.

I threaten to smooth the wrinkles out of any bastard's forehead that throws another punch, and knowing they can't keep an eye on me and each other at the same time, they retire behind the cease-fire line. Which reminds me of the bloke in the preliminary bout at the stadium in Sydney who wasn't doing too good. Between rounds his second, by way of encouragement, said, "Go on, get into him. He's not even hitting you yet," and the poor bugger replied, "Well, keep an eye on the referee then, because some bastard is."

Well, the two belligerents are standing apart facing each other, and tossing up whether to risk the bung starter flank-attack which I've threatened to mount, when a couple of hippies and a bird stroll peacefully into the bar. They take up a barrier position between the gladiators, blissfully unaware of how dangerous the ground is upon which they stand. Had the feud broken out again, the combatants would have been quite oblivious to their presence, just like two bulls fighting through a barbwire fence. However the situation is now so complicated, and with me still hefting the bung starter they decide to defer the engagement to a future date.

Seeing now that further danger of eruption is not likely, I

go over to one of the hippies and say, "Name your fodder, mister."

He must have a bit of a sense of humour (usually significantly absent with these types), because he says, "I say, boss, you don't have to threaten me to make me have a drink, I want one anyway." I then realise I am still nursing the bung starter.

I give a bit of a grin and stow the civiliser away under the counter in a convenient position for possible future use. The newcomers order up their drinks which I behead with a practised hand, and taking a long shot that they've been properly trained to take grog in its wild state, I don't put any glasses down for them.

Then I quietly tell the big bloke that if he doesn't behave himself a bit, I'll put the Dog Act on him. He takes this real serious, because he's already been through a couple of long droughts before, through playing up in the bar, and it's a bloody long way to the next pub in this region. The big bloke keeps muttering dire threats against the Irishman and what he's going to do to him but he gradually cools off, keeping in mind my threat of banishment from the pub.

Shortly after this even the dogs drift back into the bar, so I know everything is back to normal. I notice my bull terrier eyeing the hippies off, and as you can't tell from the expression on a bull terrier's face whether he's with you or agin' you, one of the hippes reaches out a hand to pat him. I suggest that such a step is not in his own best interests.

"Do you think he might bite?" he says.

"Not really, but you never know. Of course it's not the bite that hurts so much with this type of flea beater, it's prising the bastard off when he locks onto you." This hippy type has a pair of snakeproof strides on, but I know they haven't made dogproof strides yet' not for bull terriers anyway.

I tell the hippy I used to have a good sort of a bull terrier before but I had to shoot him, and he says, "Whatever for?"

I tell him it was for chasing cars.

The hippy bird chips in and says, "How dreadful. Fancy shooting a poor dog just for chasing cars."

Fair enough, I say, but the trouble was he was catching them and burying them out the back of the pub. I was having so much trouble with the coppers and the Missing Persons Bureau, that I had to shoot the dog to get *them* off my back. Even now I'm not game to dig a hole to plant a new pawpaw tree, for fear of what I'm likely to unearth.

This morbid yarn reminds me of another one, true this time, about a bloke I knew that was headed out this way years ago in his car — an old Essex or Maxwell or something like that — with no bumper bars. (They didn't have to have bumper bars in those days because people were well brought up and weren't in the habit of slamming head on into each other.) He's driving along nice and sedate when he slams into an old billy goat that's got startled by the car and jumped out of the lantana right in front of him. They didn't have four-wheel brakes then and he couldn't stop in time, so he ploughed straight into the old billy and killed him stone dead. When he gets out of the car to inspect the damage, he finds the old dead billy with his horn jammed through the radiator. When he pulls him off radiator water starts to gush out of the hole, so he has to jam him back in again while he thinks out a plan of action. The problem is there's no water for miles. His solution is to cut the goat's body away, leaving it for the dingoes and wedgetails to clean up, and then drive on slowly to the pub. He pulls up out in front here with the head still stuck in the radiator!

The hippies give a bit of a grimace and appear as though they suddenly aren't enjoying their beer so much. The bird says, "Surely he could have cut a plug for the radiator? He had a knife didn't he? Otherwise how did he cut the head off?"

Dont's be silly," I say, "how do you expect a man to cut a plug with a twist in it like an old billy stinker's horn?" But it's all too much for the hippies and they decide to shift to more genteel surroundings. They've had this place, what with all the skeletons buried out the back by the bull terrier that I shot, and the present Hound-of-the-Line sniffing around and eyeing them off as though trying to decide just where to fasten on with a whole *mouthful* of canine teeth. So they are up and off, casting a wary eye astern as they go, just in case the bull terrier decides to overcome his inhibitions. Which shows how little they know about these animated mincing machines. I only have to sic him on, and he'll go out and bring the three of them back in again, and keep them here until they shout for the bar.

Talking about shouting for the bar, I suddenly come back to reality and find that there isn't much activity in the drinking line, so I say, "Righto, whose bung is it?" and for once in his life the big bloke pokes his bib in and claims the honour. I am nearly going to suggest that it go in the *Guiness Book of Records*, but think better of it, in case the big bastard reneges.

He startles me further by saying, "You have one too, boss," This last bit, calling me boss, fairly shakes me, as I'm used to him calling me all sorts of names, most of them uncomplimentary. However, to save further ill-feeling I behead one for myself when I get the drinks for the mob. I'm pleased in a way that he and the Irishman have apparently buried the hatchet, but somehow or other I'm convinced that the tomahawks is in a very shallow grave.

I hardly get a sip out of my stubby after saying cheers to the big blokes and clinking stubbies with the Irishman (which is a dangerous practice to which I seldom subscribe owing to the danger of breakage and loss of all that goodness), when who should appear but my missus. She has one quick glance and says, "At it again, eh?"

"Christ, a man can't win," I say. "Here I've been for hours pulling my arm nearly out of its socket knocking heads off stubbies; putting up with way-out types; breaking up fights; listening to all the intrigue which is only another name for bastardry; listening to all the prevarication which is only a refined way of saying bullshit . . . and the first time a man has a drink, you're clambering on his back like a bloody goanna escaping a pack of hounds.

"All right, all right, don't carry on. I know you're a victim."

"Arrgh, a man *needs* a drink, having to put up with all these morons."

The Irishman pipes up and says, "Who's a moron? This big bloke here might be one, but not me."

I hear the scrape of bar stools which is the usual prelude to violent action in the bar, so I grab for the bung starter and come out with it in one hand and a claw hammer in the other.

"What are you going to do with that?" says somebody.

"If these blokes get back into their corners I'm just going to repair this persuader of mine," and I start to gently hammer the wedge back into the handle of the bung starter. This is what is known as the power of suggestion. The missus, who'd started it all, fades back into her rightful province in the kitchen. Then old Bill the tin scratcher says, "Why don;t you chuck these two bastards a bone and give them something to really fight over?"

The Irishman turns on him and calls him a mean-natured hoary-headed old bastard.

Bill objects strongly to this charge as he says he's not all *that* ancient, because he's only been drawing the old-age pension for twenty-five years.

The Irishman says he hopes the old bloke has got a bit left out of the pension cheque because it's his bung. The old bloke says he hasn't got any left, but he'll still shout, as he can get a bit of credit off me. I give it to him too and set the drinks up. I hope when this old bloke departs this madhouse for keeps he does it on a Thursday, because the pension cheque arrives late on Wednesday and I don't want to be in *too* deep when he cools off.

He's been in the bush that long that he's right out of touch with world affairs, and he sort of lives in the past a bit. The old bloke came out of hibernation once just after World War II, and says, "How's the war going?" and I say it's over.

"Who won?" he says, and I assure him that we did.

"Thank Christ," he says, "I never did like those bloody Boers."

Just then a hippy type slinks into the bar and asks for a stubby. He's so allergic to water that he must fairly cringe even crossing a bridge. I see the Irishman eye him off, then pointedly shift along about the distance of two bar stools. Old Bill doesn't shift however; he's that high himself he doesn't notice anything out of order. He only has a tin scratcher's wash when he comes to town — a change of shirt — and the fact that you could nearly grow sweet spuds on the newcomer's hide is no novelty to him. Anyway, the hippie downs his drink and moves on.

Then the Irishman tells us about another old bloke, a tin

scratcher (a dry blower who came down from Mt Garnet), who fell in the creek one day and got a chill . . . because this was only the second time he'd ever got water on him. The first time was when he was christened. The chill proved serious enough to bring him into the hospital in Cooktown. The sisters and nurses held a stop-work meeting over him as he was so grubby. They finally decided that instead of handling him with tongs, they'd give him a good scrub down. They did this, and found a singlet that the old bloke thought he'd lost years before.

I chip in now and tell them about another bloke they scrubbed down in hospital. Apart from finding two singlets and a pair of jockey shorts he didn't know about, they also unearthed a *school bag*.

The Irishman says, "OK, you win. I'll buy a round on the strength of that one."

Well, by now I seem to have got the Irishman and the big bloke settled down. The night is wearing on and I'm really starting to feel the pinch. It seems there's no end to the jobs a poor bloody publican has to do. It doesn't matter how well the pub is paying, the publican is still underpaid. Not only have you got to keep the grog up to the mob and feed the bastards as and when required, but you have to referee manfights and supervise dogfights, as well as listen to all their bloody whinges. You've got to soak up all the bullshit they ladle out, and see you don't get touched in the process; go and snig cars out of bogs, and fill bloody petrol tanks any hour hour of the day and night. If you can't see the funny side of things, you're buggered. Especially like a few nights ago when I'm coming home in the ute. I suddenly have a no-go engine and it's raining cats and dogs. It's dark as the inside of a dog's guts, and a man's trying to make a major engine repair with a blunt screwdriver and a pair of snotty-nosed pliers. To make matters worse the grog has cut out. Anyway, just then a joker comes along, and he's got an esky full of ice-cold Fourex stubbies — and the situation changes dramatically. After we jerk a couple of these into us, I try the engine again. Bugger me if it doesn't go. Must've been all it needed all along. I tell this joker to follow me down to the Den and we'd top his bunkers up again.

Apart from all the other problems, a man has to try to

keep things a bit clean and tidy, which is a full-time job for an ordinary sort of bloke. If you didn't, the mob would soon have the place in the same state as their own joints, just to make them feel at home.

Then at this time of the year, you've got to run Melbourne Cup sweeps and collect the dough, then draw the bloody things. If you're ever lucky enough to win a sweep, the bludgers say you must've rigged it. Then there's the women accusing you of getting their particular Old Man on the grog when the bastard concerned's never been off it since he started sneaking around the back of the pubs at age fifteen.

There's the odd jobs like fishing a bloke's tats out of the urinal where he's ejected them with a surplus of turps. You take them out and give them a good hosing down on the lawn. You present him with them, and he doesn't even mutter thanks to you, just sticks them back in his gob, not even enquiring where they've been to all this time. He's the same bloke who'll whinge about the quality of the tucker, or about the bloody breakfast bacon being too salty.

Which reminds me of the old publican in Port Douglas who found a set of dentures (he didn't say where), and put a notice up on the blackboard under Found, reading, "One set of dentures. Apply within, without".

A man has to be on his toes all the time to stay in front. This reminds me of the production line manager who was told by an efficiency expert to get all the workers on their toes, so he raised the urinal six inches. I don't need any trick like that to get on my toes; all I have to do is to deal with the general public. You only have to relax for a moment for some urger to have a go at you in an unguarded moment, or knock off the till while you're out the back answering a call of nature.

Of course this last little enterprise is not confined to this pub, as evidenced by the notice one publican put up in Cairns: "Wanted, a smart barmaid, not TOO bloody smart".

Then you have to put up with all the blokes who want you to contribute to something or other, and when you only chuck in twenty cents cringe because they can't stand the sound of metal, preferring the quiet rustle of a note which is more soothing to their nerves.

Then there are the Bush Baptists and Holy Rollers. These

urgers will have a go at you every day of the week, holidays included, to try to convert you. Then you get all the priests and gurus wanting you to shell out good hard cash for their cause, at the same time trying to frighten hell out of you, and telling you that only the good go to heaven.

From what I've seen of the mob so far, it looks like heaven's going to be a terribly lonely place and old Peter might have to shut the skytel down for the want of business. All the little angels sitting round on wispy clouds listlessly strumming harps will wonder when Peter is going to wake up to himself and import a bit of permissiveness into the joint to boost trade.

You get the well-dressed urger who comes into the bar and shouts for the mob with a bouncy cheque and even the rubber in it is synthetic. I've got so many of them stuck up on the bar wall so far I'm thinking about bringing out a new brand of wall paper with a string of dud cheques as the main motif, for pub use only. That way we could get all these smart buggers' names stuck up in every hotel in the country.

There's always the bloody merchants on your back, ringing you up and asking when you're going to send a cheque down to clear the account, and you've only just got the bloody bill by the pack-horse mail and haven't had time to check it yet — even if you had the inclination. But you have to cop these blokes and play it real cool, because if they cut off the grog supply a man'd be in more trouble than Woolworths with a brahman bull loose in the supermarket.

Besides all this, a man has to put up with the bloody bureaucrats as well, and this is about the hardest of all because you can't put the Dog Act on *them* — they'll put it on *you* if you don't look out. You've got the Health Inspector peering into toilet bowls and grease traps and under beds and things, until you wonder if he's lost his wallet with a copy of his rich uncle's will in it. Having looked in all the likely places, he makes a thorough search and looks in the unlikely places. Then he gets up you about the state of the joint and raises hell because you've got a pig in the backyard getting fattened up for Christmas.

All this fuss about one lone, motherless pig. There's hundreds of the buggers running wild around the place after we all go to bed, coming in to pick up the windfall mangoes, which I'd have to clean up in the morning if they didn't. They usually sign for what they take too, and a man's got to get up early and clean up all the signatures, as well as the rotten mangoes the fussy buggers don't eat. The stray cows come round for a few mangoes as well, and they leave a bigger signature than the bloody pigs.

Then you have to put up with the coppers breathing down your neck, and closing the bar up at legal closing time, just when you've got a bunch of free-spending mad ringers and look like making a quid. The Licensing Inspector bobs up with no warning whatsoever, and starts poking his bloody nose into everything, and you know when he leaves he's going to give you an Order. You don't know what it's going to be, but you know it's going to be "something". Probably tell you to paint the joint out, and it's already been painted out about twenty-seven years ago when they used to make real paint. The paint will probably last the old joint out because it's getting on for a century since the first publican here started to make the tin miners a bit sillier than they were to start with. (My missus says that the bloke that drinks beer only pours it from one mug into another, and she could be right at that.)

The worst type of all we get here is from the Income Tax department, and as a dyed-in-the-wool bureaucrat, and standover merchant to boot, he's a winner. He's usually a lizard-lidded urger and backed up by a lizard-lidded mate of the same calibre. He and his mate pull all your nice figures to pieces and make cabalistic signs in your ledger. He wants to know how many house guests we had last night, and I try to add up how many walking wounded I saw at first light this morning to arrive at a reasonable figure. Because I'm a bit long arriving at a figure, the bastard thinks I'm trying to be evasive.

Then he wants to know how I can account for about fifty cartons of lager which don't show up in any return. I say I must've drunk them, but he's an unbelievable sort of a son of a bitch and I can see he won't wear that one. After all, that's only a carton a week, barely enough to wash a man's mouth out with. Then he gets up me about a dozen cases of whiskey that also don't tally on the sheet he's got and he says, "Don't tell me you drank that too,'' and I say, "Listen mister, I can spill that much in a financial year, without trying."

They keep getting into me until I'm nearly raw all over, and red-rimmed round the eyes like an old brahman bull infested with buffalo flies. I can see they don't believe a word I say, but of course, they're Unbelievers to start with, having come from a long line of Unbelievers, specially hand-picked for the job from a queue of applicant Unbelievers.

Finally they get through with all their leading questions, and they sort of indicate that I can shoot through — the big-hearted bastards. They go into a huddle over the books and *I* go into the bar for a heart-starter. Later on they ooze their way into the bar and order a couple of stubbies, but I don't shout for them for fear they might hang a bribery charge on me along with what other charges the mean-natured buggers have thought up.

Besides, they might ask me next year when they come round, how to account for two stubbies not otherwise accounted for. They'd be mean enough. I've got a sign in the bar that reads, "I shoot every third salesman that comes into this bar . . . the second has just left". After these two urgers depart I amend it to read Income Tax Investigator instead of Salesman. Must remember to scrub it though before the buggers come round again, because they belong to a particular breed, totally deficient in even the rudiments of humour.

So now you see something of what a poor bloody bush pulican has to put up with. To top it all, if the missus comes in and catches me having a couple of double whiskeys to fortify my flagging strength, she gets on a man's back as well. Sometimes I think it'd be far easier to end it all, and if ever it comes over me that I'm going to, I'll do it just before the bloody Irishman comes down from the hills if I can only get fair warning.

Anyway I'm jerked back into the present by some bloke who comes into the bar. After ordering up he asks me how I'm going, and I tell him I'm afraid I'm going to live.

"Christ man," he says, "you really mean you don't want to?"

"Not forever. Fancy having to put up with a bunch of bloody misfits and morons like this crowd here forever."

The Irishman jumps off his bar stool and starts on me: "Listen you, you four-eyed hoary-headed old bast . . . all right, all right, I'll take it back." He's seen the bung starter coming out into the ready-use position. It's not the bung starter he's afraid of so much as the Dog Act I've got to back it up. He's never been through a drought yet — not in this pub anyway — and he's not taking the risk, because if there's one disease this bloke's afraid of, it's dehydration. It can be fatal to any well-seasoned stubby drinker if the condition is brought on too suddenly. It's not a disease at all of course, just a state you can get in; either by misadventure, or by plain bull-headed stupidity. Never let the grog die in you, mate; this way you can avoid all hangovers.

I decide not to end it all because I suddenly remember that I have a good sort of a Cup double in the making. I've already got the first leg up in the Caufield Cup, and I've got Rain Lover in the Melbourne Cup leg. I know that the rest of the field couldn't beat him if they started the day before. So I shoo the mob out of the bar like a flock of neighbour's fowls so a man can get in a bit of much-needed rest for Cup day, which is tomorrow.

I know it's going to be a pretty hard day anyway, and I also know the Irishman and several others have got the first leg up in the double too, so if old Rain Lover gets home it'll be a harder day still, followed by a hard day's night.

Usually by the time it comes to close the bar, the drunks are full enough to be cantakerous and a bit stubborn about getting kicked out. Tonight for some strange reason, they all take it quiet docilely, including the big bloke who normally is about as easy to shift as a short-footed mule.

Well, next morning I get up early and there's the bloody Irishman thumping on the bar door like Ivan the Terrible hammering on the Gates of Constantinople, but he doesn't want to sack the joint, he only wants a rum to get his heart settled to a regular beat again. I give him one, but don't have one myself, showing great restraint because of the big day ahead. I make the Irishman go out to the dining room and get the nosebag on, because without a bit of tucker, no drunk can carry on, however good he is at sinking grog.

Suddenly there's a newcomer in the bar — how he got in I don't know, but he's there.

"Would you like some breakfast too?"

"What's on?"

"Mystery bags."

"For Christ's sake what's that?"

"I've been eating them for years," I tell him, "The butcher makes them in town out of all the bits of meat he sweeps off the floor that have fallen off the chopping blocks — the sawdust's included. Then he chucks all the bits of fat he cuts off the point of the T-bone steaks (after he's weighed it first of course), then he chucks in a batch of herbs which is a sort of dried grass, then a couple of mouldy old leftover loaves from the baker (this is to make up the weight), then a handful of salt, all knobbly and not crunched up nice and fine. He pokes all this stuff into a thing called a mincing machine, plus a bucketful of pigs' whistles. (They don't waste anything of the old pig except the grunts.) Then he cuts up bits of bullocks' guts and stuffs this mixture into them and ties both ends of the bullocks' guts to keep the stuff in. That's what takes the time and makes them so expensive — tying all the ends of the things. Then they're ready to eat . . . after you cook them of course."

"Wellarbybuggid." says the bloke. "Some people would come at anythin'. I don't think I want any breakfast, thanks just the same."

After that we pass the time peacefully until we get the final acceptances over the radio. Like I said before, at this time of the year the poor mug who runs the pub's expected to run the sweeps, so now I have to get stuck into the clerical work of typing out all the names of everyone who's chucked in over the past few weeks, along with the horses' names. Then I cut them all up into hats and we're ready to draw the sweeps. We can't draw yet without a couple of independent witnesses. If we did, and happened to win, the mob would be likely to think the game stunk a bit. So we defer the drawing until somebody else shows up. Finally, as the usual crowd starts to drift in, we start the drawing, picking out names from one hat, and matching them up with horses, hairy goats, hobbled ducks and ones that are only in there to make up the numbers from the other hat.

Between doing this and serving a bit of grog as required, which is just about all the time, the morning passes peacefully enough because the big bloke isn't there to stir the Irishman up and get him using naughty words. Not that he needs much stirring up to get him going; it just comes out of him naturally, but without the necessary opposition he's a spent force — about as effective as a Tibetan admiral in charge of a detachment of Japanese horse marines.

The day wears on, and apart from betting on the Cup we give the other races a bit of attention with every second bugger wanting me to put some money on something or other with four legs on it, until I look like running out of dough in my phone account at the TAB. If this happens, it looks like I'll have to do a bit a SP on the side, which I don't want to do because nearly anything can win in the Melbourne Cup.

Finally it comes round to Cup time and the mob is hanging on every word coming over the radio. The starter must be mucking around like an old battler at a christening because he's taking a hell of a long time to get the horses settled down. Some of them are playing up a bit. Must've got too many lollies.

Reminds me of the time at the Cooktown races, when a steward caught one of the owners giving his horse something just before the race. The owner with great presence of mind says, "They're only lollies. He just likes sugar. here, have a couple yourself." The owner gobbles a couple of these "lollies" to prove they're not harmful. The old stipe is still a bit suspicious; but from the taste of them he decides that's all they are, just lollies.

Then the owner gives his final instructions to the hoop, and he says, "As soon as they jump, 'go for the doctor'. If anything passes you in the straight, don't worry. It's only going to be me or the steward."

Anyway, finally they stop molling around down at Flemington and we hear Joe Brown saying they are away to a good start. You don't take much notice of what he's saying for a long time, because he's got to keep talking to fill in time and two miles is a bloody long way to go. Everyone is keyed up to concert pitch, and when I hear the rising inflection in old Joe's voice, I start to take more interest. Once I hear him say that Rain Lover has the lead, I know it's all over. He gets so far in front that you'd have had to take a photo with a fish-eye lens to get him and the rest of the horses in the same picture.

It's only the sagacity of the judge that decides that he's the winner, instead of a straggler from the previous race.

Anyway, finally the numbers go up, but I'm too busy dishing out grog by now to hear them. I've already heard all I want to know because for once I've got in front of the bookies with my double, and I know the Irishman has also got the double and a bit more on the TAB. It's only a loan of course from the books, as they'll get it all back, but a man might as well make use of loan money while he's got the chance. So I chuck ten dollars into a plastic icecream container and the Irishman does the same. A couple of the smaller winners chuck in odd bits until there's about fifty bucks in kitty, which is enough to start with. From now on no-one shouts in the bar, and we take it out of kitty.

It's bloody amazing how the word goes round when the free grog is on. There are faces in the bar that I've never seen before . . . they must've crawled out of a hollow log or something. You don't have to ring a bell or beat a drum to call them up when there's free grog on. Then the festivities start in dead ernest. I can see this celebration is going to go on for some time. The bar is filling up until she's bulging at the seams and the "ringers retreat" is full too. There's a fair overflow into the mango lounge on the verandah and there are a few dog scuffles because every other mug has to bring his dog to listen to the Cup, and there's not a racing dog amongst them.

When things get really warmed up, I notice my blue heeler standing to one side with a look of absolute puzzlement on his face, wondering what it's all about and how his boss can get so lowbrow as to encourage a bunch of morons and deadbeats like this to come to the joint. We've even got a sprinkling of hippes hanging round, neglecting their grass patch in the hills. The rest of the crowd have come from near and far — some of them even from Darwin and another bloke from New Guinea; this last bloke desperately wants to shout the bar. We tell him there's no need to, which is something new in his experience, but later on when kitty gets a bit light on we let him shout. Costs a bit too, but he doesn't seem to mind. Must have a good sort of a dollar tree somewhere.

Not long after that I dive my hand into kitty and bottom on plastic, so I take the first note I can find in the till and chuck it into kitty as a sort of nest egg, and I give the icecream container to the Irishman to go round and collect a bit more loot. He goes round shaking it under everyone's nose like a Salvation Army lass jiggling the collection box, but he can't make the same rattling noise that she does to get attention because there's no shrapnel in this, only notes.

Even if this modern dollar currency does look like Jap Invasion money, you've still got to have the stuff, and the bank seems to accept it as OK. Personally I never use the stuff except in the TAB — they go for it there. If I want to buy anything for real money I just write a cheque. Still, I've got to make the books balance, and the Irishman comes back shortly with the icecream barrel stuffed with notes, and we all get stuck into it a second time. It looks as though it's going to be a hard day's night all right.

The day wears on into night. The missus comes in and plonks the hind leg of a roast pig on the loungeroom table, along with a couple of sharp knives, and the mob hookes into it as if eating was about to be banned. The way some of them are going for it — like pigs — it's the nearest thing to an act of cannibalism I've seen for a long time.

On and on the evening goes. Night wears on into the next day, and I see that the crowd is thinning out a bit, so I send the Irishman round with the icecream bucket to scoop up a bit more loot before they thin out too much, and he brings back enough for the final sitting. We've got through the period without any fights (I haven't had to bring the old bung starter out once yet), and a good time has been had by all, and mostly on bookies' dough for a change.

About three a.m. I shoo them all out (takes a bit of doing of course), and shut the old Den up as tight as a drum and threaten instant horrible death to any bastard that wakes me up before daylight. Just after daylight, I hear a fair sort of a hammering noise and decide it's Ivan the Terrible, that bloody Irishman.

There's only two ways out of this I decide; either shoot this bastard or myself, whichever is the less painful. I'm that crook from the grog. I think the latter might be the more acceptable solution but I haven't a gun handy, so I drag myself out of bed and abuse the cat for stomping around the room rattling hell out of a man's nerves. I select the right key on the bunch with unerring accuracy, and open the bar and let the Irishman in, and he needn't bloody well think I'm doing this all for his sake either.

As I go behind the counter I snatch a bottle of Macleay Duff off the shelf because I know it's going to take more than a Get Well card to put me right, and I just can't look a stubby of beer in the neck. We settle in for a quiet little session and it's just about soaked through to the fingertips when the missus comes in unexpectantly, and says. "Can't you fellows *ever* leave it alone?" and I tell her that this is purely for medicinal purposes.

"You'd better come and have some breakfast' RIGHT NOW."

So I tip what is left in the scotch bottle into the two glasses — it isn't worth putting back onto the shelf — toss the bottle into the Out basket under the counter, and we go in and put the nosebag on.

While these cliff-dwellers on the shores of Lake Burley Griffin are mucking round with the Constitution, they could get onto the Attorney-General's back to formulate a new bill of rights for the publican as well, and if they nutted it out carefully enough, it'd just about exonerate him from everything. (Except paying the licence fee, and of course satisfying those income tax bloodhounds; there's no hope they'd ever get to that stage.) A publician's rights could be in fine print on the back of the pub licence, like on the back of a shipping receipt. Some of the main provisions would be to allow the publican to set dingo traps and lay baits for the inspectorial fraternity, with suitable indemnity against legal action if you happened to get something outside your sphere — like a stock inspector or a weights and measures blokes, or an airport inspector off his normal beat.

That'd be a problem of course, there being so many of the bastards these days. Now that they've got all these national parks, conservation areas, restricted fishing zones, murri cave-painting forbidden areas and so on there are so many "can't-do-its" to the square peninsulametre, that a man nearly wants a licence to fart in the area. I sometimes wonder if we shouldn't give the place back to the murris and apologise for the state it's in. I'm just waiting to see the ultimate in inspectors. He's sure to bob up soon . . . the inspector to inspect inspectors. You'd have to dive right down to the bottom of the barrel to get *him*.

But back to the bill of rights. There'd have to be a clause for the bouncy cheque blokes with an automatic sentence when caught — a stretch of six moons at Dunlop or Goodyear with no pay or leave entitlements, just to give him a proper gutful of the smell of rubber. (I doubt that it'd cure the bastard just the same, as this trait is built into his genes.) He'd have to work every day too, and when production ceased through the rest of the crowd going on strike, he'd still have to be on the job, cutting cheque-sized pieces of rubber out of a big sheet (preferably with a knife and fork, just to make it bloody difficult) and then signing them with a blunt six-inch nail.

One of the main provisions of course, would be to give the publician authority to shoot troublesome customers (under extreme provocation of course). They could have a sort of points system for the trouble-makers like they have for driving licences. The whole thing would entail having a private burial-ground out the back of the pub. It would have to be ready marked-out with numbered plots with a sketch plan to be included in the survey of the licensed area.

A bloke wouldn't have to shoot many really, as the rest of them would soon get the message. Any joker that was performing in the bar, and getting a bit short on points, you could ask quietly what his plot number was on the back. Of course the publician should have the power to extend the points system with purse men, or good spenders like mad ringers with a six months cheque to bust. This includes tin scratchers who've just had a good "clean up", not that I'd *want* to shoot the Irishman anyhow. I'd sooner put him in a time capsule (a 500 year one), just to show future generations what a poor bloody downtrodden, twentieth century publican had to put up with, and to partly explain the high incidence of nervous breakdowns among hoteliers.

In a way, it'd be a low, mean act, to let this bugger loose in 500 years time on an unsuspecting public without suitable warning. Not that you could really give them sufficient advance warning; they wouldn't believe you.

Yes, I'm going to get onto the Licensed Victuallers' Association about this business — the bill of publicans' rights, I mean. We ought to get it written into the bill that we're all in line for mention in the New Year's Honours list, for long and meritorous service to the public. They should strike a special medal for any of us that have put up with the bastards for more than twenty years, then give a bar to the decoration for the bloke that has cleaned out the most troublemakers, because this is one aspect of public service that's likely to be overlooked. I've only been in the game ten years, but having to work overtime putting up with the Irishman is enough to bring my seniority up to date.

Thus I rest my case. Actually, after reading all this tripe again, I realise there's sure to be a lot of blokes after my blood, so I think I'd better write it under a nom de plume, which is a sort of makeshift umbrella invented by a half-baked Frenchman, which you get under when you're expecting a shower of shit. Yes, I think I'd better do that.

PINISH

1/265
4870
I SHOOT EVERY THIRD INCOME TAX INSPECTOR ~~SALESMAN~~ THAT COMES INTO THIS BAR. THE SECOND HAS JUST LEFT.

Epilogue

My wife, who continues to suffer me (gladly or otherwise), said to me after reading the manuscript of this book, "Why didn't you write this years ago?"

I gave it a bit of thought and said, "Dunno. Maybe I never got sober enough before . . . and have you ever tried to work *two* typewriters at once?"

In all we did a stretch of thirteen years in the Den (no time off for good behaviour either), and despite the demanding work of running the pub with little or no outside help, life was generally a rather pleasant experience.

We were situated about 500 feet above sea level and enjoyed a rather equable climate, free of mosquitos and sandflies. The grove of mango trees surrounding the hotel tended to minimise the trying conditions of tropical summer temperatures, and the high rainforest-clad mountains in front of it presented a wonderful scenic view all seasons of the year. The property had a full river frontage at the back on the Annan River, a permanent and beautiful stream.

The original owner of the hotel, Jack Ross, who had a tin mine in the mountains in front of it, on one occasion took on as a labourer a stowaway who had jumped ship in Cooktown. His name was Daniel and one day when he was standing at the tunnel mouth Jack thought of Daniel in the lion's den and named the mine accordingly. Later the name gravitated to the hotel.

It was only the flourishing tourist trade that forced my wife and I to sell. The increased workload became too great for us to handle. We had made many friends among those who visited use regularly from near and distant parts, and of course the inevitable odd enemy, a tiny minority who, give the world, would complain because there was no fence around it.

The old Den is still going (1989), now approaching the century mark, and the present licensee, Doug Green, and his wife Mary, are carrying on the age-old traditions of the country pub. It wll be a sad day for many if those traditions disappear and we hear no more the ringing call: "Righto! Whose bung is it?"

After seeing all the deadbeats, weirdoes, and irresponsible nong-nongs that have frequented the old Den over the years, I am forced to the conclusion that planet earth would have to be the dumping ground for all the misfits and drop-outs from other and more stable planets, otherwise we simply could not have got such a mixed-up crowd around to confront us.

The funny part of it is that you can never see two of these comedians that act and look the same. Planet earth would certainly be the refuse tip of the universe, from which has evolved a new sub-species, which nevertheless has also developed a sense of humour — and that is about all that saves us. More power to them!